Volume 27

AERODYNAMICS

IMMUNOLOGY

THE NEW
how it works

*Fiber optic cables used in modern communications
systems transmit signals as pulses of light
more efficiently than copper cables.*
Photo: Dominique Sarraute
The Image Bank

THE *NEW* ILLUSTRATED
Science and Invention
ENCYCLOPEDIA

The Modern World

A COMPREHENSIVE REVIEW of the major sciences with particular emphasis
on developing and evolving technologies as well as new discoveries
about our natural world. The articles which are arranged
alphabetically were specially written for this edition
and are accompanied by dynamic, full-color
photographs, drawings and diagrams
that offer new insight into the
modern world and all
its wonders.

H. S. STUTTMAN INC. *Publishers*   Westport, Connecticut 06880

Contents

Volume 27

Published by H. S. STUTTMAN INC.
Westport, Connecticut 06889
© Marshall Cavendish Limited 1993

INTRODUCTION

DURING THE PAST CENTURY the world has witnessed a pace of technological advancement that has been unprecedented. Today, once again, the world stands on the brink of an explosion in science and technology – for scientific achievement never stands still and each new discovery provides yet another platform for even further development.

And this development can be at bewildering speed – in electronics the pace is such that obsolescence of personal computers is close to less than a year. Advances in medical technology are increasing as well. By using electronics technology as a stepping stone, advances are being made daily – new diagnostic techniques and equipment, treatments, and discoveries are all being made available to improve our quality of life.

THE MODERN WORLD provides you with an insider's view of all the creative breakthroughs to come – a permanent record of the marvels that will transform your world and your children's world. Equally important, it provides the background leading up to these advances as well as outlining their likely effects on our lives.

This supplement to THE NEW ILLUSTRATED SCIENCE AND INVENTION ENCYCLOPEDIA – HOW IT WORKS provides full details of the very latest developments in more than 100 sciences. Scientists and science writers have combined their talents to illuminate the frontiers of science in a lucid, well organized style that makes it easily assimilated by a broad spectrum of readers.

In some sciences, such as *Particle Physics*, the work being carried out is at the forefront of our knowledge and discoveries are being made almost annually. In others, such as *Civil Engineering*, the timescale is much longer: designs and techniques that are on the drawing board today will not take shape for years. But in each case, THE MODERN WORLD will give details of current research – and future developments.

These extensively illustrated volumes have been thoroughly researched to include the latest scientific concepts and developments and will form a valuable, lasting addition to THE NEW ILLUSTRATED SCIENCE AND INVENTION ENCYCLOPEDIA – HOW IT WORKS for both the technically informed and non-specialist reader.

The foundation of THE MODERN WORLD is twofold: first, it has an easily understandable, yet detailed and authoritative text written by experts. Second, these volumes feature extensive use of informative color photographs and drawings that complement the text and enhance the usefulness of the work as a valuable learning aid.

The articles are divided into multi-page key articles that describe major sciences from *Aerodynamics* to *Zoology*. At the end of the second volume are briefer articles on subsidiary fields, such as *Astrometry* and *Kinetics*. Both sections are arranged alphabetically and are profusely illustrated. Articles within these two volumes are cross-referenced with SMALL CAPITALS and the work includes a comprehensive index to the two volumes.

Many of the photographs in THE MODERN WORLD could not have been taken just a few years ago. It is now possible, using the scanning tunneling microscope, to make images of individual atoms, while at the other end of the scale, astronomers are finding structures that existed shortly after the Big Bang that created the Universe. Some of the illustrations come directly from the scientists involved in the research and are published here for the first time, even before publication in academic journals.

The aim of this work is to provide both the specialist and non-specialist reader with a guide to current scientific thought and development. It is designed to stimulate the mind and in doing so may create more questions than it answers. If so, then it will have succeeded in ensuring, in a small way, our continued quest to understand the world in which we live.

THE MODERN WORLD is an invaluable supplement to THE NEW ILLUSTRATED SCIENCE AND INVENTION ENCYCLOPEDIA – HOW IT WORKS, both broadening the scope of the work and enhancing its usefulness.

THE PUBLISHERS

Left: The Keck telescope on Mauna Kea, Hawaii, completed in 1992, is the first of a new generation of telescopes that should push forward the frontiers of our understanding of the universe.

Aerodynamics

Aerodynamics – the study of air flow – has entered a phase of slow refinement after decades in which great advances were made. Today, aircraft designers are still extracting performance improvements from two innovations now over 20 years old – the supercritical aerofoil section and the winglet.

Two challenges remain for the 1990s – to reduce subsonic aircraft drag significantly and to produce efficient supersonic transportation. The former goal looks achievable, the latter less so – at least not economically, and not in this decade.

The supercritical wing is among the most influential recent advances in aerodynamics. Its aerofoil section shape delays the increase in drag which begins when shock waves form, allowing the aircraft to fly faster and more efficiently.

The winglet has been equally widely exploited. This wingtip aerofoil turns wasted energy in the vortex of air cast off by the wing into useful thrust, and also offsets the drag which accompanies lift.

The key to significantly reducing subsonic aircraft drag lies in achieving laminar flow – a smooth flow, with no whirlpool-like eddies. The airflow over a wing is generally turbulent, except near the leading edge where it is still laminar. Turbulent flow causes more drag, but laminar flow is fragile, as it exists only in a layer a few millimeters thick close to the wing surface.

Certain aerofoil sections can sustain laminar flow over more of the wing, at least while the aircraft is cruising. Natural laminar flow, as this technology is called, is being applied already to business jets to reduce drag. But preventing the transition to turbulent flow is difficult during take-off and landing, when the wing is working hard.

Large aircraft, such as commercial airliners and military transports, pose a greater problem. Their large wings generally have movable leading edges to increase lift during take-off and landing. When these devices retract during the cruise they leave gaps which can trigger turbulent flow.

The answer is to sustain laminar flow artificially by suction. Called hybrid laminar flow control, this damps out disturbances in the thin layer of smooth airflow, delaying the transition to turbulent flow. The turbulent air is siphoned off through thousands of tiny, laser-drilled holes in the forward part of the wing surface.

Problems with laminar flow control

Laminar flow can be disrupted by small imperfections in the wing surface, such as ice and insects which can also block the suction holes. Wings will require regular cleaning, possibly before every flight. The wing profile must be smooth, requiring very tight tolerances during manufacture.

Questions remain over the range of wing sizes, sweep angles, and aircraft speeds at which natural laminar flow can be maintained and those at which hybrid laminar flow control will be required. The U.S. and Europe are locked in a race to perfect the technology, sensing that to be first will be to gain a significant commercial advantage.

Hybrid laminar flow control is also under con-

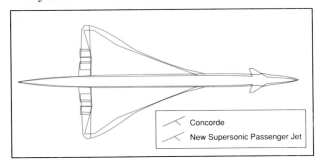

Concorde
New Supersonic Passenger Jet

Above: The design of Concorde compared with that of its proposed successor, a 280-seat trans-Pacific supersonic airliner known as AST. The design was published in 1990.
Left: The F-16 XL fighter with modified wing in flight. This experimental setup was successful in creating laminar flow over a large section of the wing, holding the promise of considerable fuel savings in commercial aircraft.

sideration for the second generation of supersonic transportation. The Anglo-French Concorde is widely regarded as being aerodynamically inefficient, with its delta wing optimized for cruising at twice the speed of sound (Mach 2). On take-off and landing, the wing generates considerable drag which must be overcome by increasing engine thrust. As a result, Concorde is noisy.

A second-generation supersonic transport will not happen unless it can be made as quiet as, or quieter than, today's subsonic airliners. While much depends on developing new JET TECHNOLOGY, a critical factor in the success of Concorde's successor will be its overall aerodynamic efficiency.

A new wing design

In studies over a number of years a configuration has been evolved for the next supersonic transport which uses an "arrow" wing. The inner part of the wing is much like that of Concorde, broad and highly swept. The outer sections on each side are more like a conventional wing. The resulting wing is shaped like an arrowhead.

The advantage of this wing shape is that it combines the Mach 2-plus cruise efficiency of Concorde's delta wing with the low-speed performance of a subsonic wing complete with moving leading and trailing edges like that of a 747 wing to increase lift during take-off and landing. The arrow wing is inevitably a compromise, and one

designers are keen to improve.

Supersonic laminar flow control is one avenue currently being explored by designers. NASA has fitted two arrow-wing F-16XL fighters with a test surface, or "glove", on the inner, highly swept sections of their left wings. These gloves are covered with laser-drilled holes through which the turbulent flow is siphoned off. Flight test results from these planes show that laminar flow can be sustained at supersonic speeds.

Another major problem facing designers of a supersonic transport is to find ways of reducing the sonic boom heard on the ground as the aircraft flies supersonically over land.

One area of research continues to define what level of sonic-boom "overpressure" is acceptable to people on the ground. At present, Concorde aircraft are permitted to fly supersonically only over the sea and unpopulated areas.

Designers are also testing low-boom configurations in wind tunnels. Low-boom designs use modified arrow wings which stretch from the nose to the tail. This spreads the lift over a longer wing and reduces shock-wave strength and therefore sonic-boom intensity.

Economics, and not technology, will determine whether a second-generation supersonic transport emerges, as hoped, early next century. The work now under way will, however, shape generations of aircraft to come.

Below: The ideal air flow over a wing is laminar, as shown here. This, however, is an ideal case and practical wings often produce turbulent flow, which creates drag and reduces efficiency.

Above: The wing of an F-16 XL fighter being modified in an experiment to achieve laminar air flow. The dark section on the left is a modified titanium wing section, with millions of tiny laser-cut holes. This is surrounded by a larger area of fiberglass which blends the experimental section to the wing.

Aerospace engineering

Aerospace has always been a "leading edge" technology. Developments made by aerospace engineers have later been adopted by the designers of anything from cars to refrigerators. The main branches of aerospace engineering are AERODYNAMICS, propulsion (see JET TECHNOLOGY), materials, structures, systems (especially avionics), and special topics for particular classes of airplane.

Since the 1930s most airplanes have been made of aluminum and its alloys, and today special alloys of aluminum and lithium are enabling airframes (the main structures) to be stronger and lighter. Where the stresses are highest the only answer is ultra-high-strength steel, and where a part has to bear heavy loads at high temperatures designers often use titanium. Modern passenger jets have to be designed to withstand 60,000 or more hours of bending and flexing in rough air. Not only does the structure have to resist fatigue but there also have to be duplicate load paths, so that, if one part cracks, another will still carry the load until the cracked part is replaced.

Composite materials

Since 1966 fiber-reinforced composites have increasingly replaced metal. A composite can be thought of as millions of fibers, each thinner than a human hair, stuck together with adhesive. Most fibers are made from carbon or a spider-web material called Kevlar™.

Switching from metal to a composite reduces weight, dramatically slashes the number of parts, and eliminates fatigue problems. The entire wing of the Harrier II jump jet is made of a carbon composite material. Airbus pioneered with the carbon fin of its A310 wide-body, and now the entire tail ends of the A320, 330, and 340 are carbon.

For many years materials-physicists have been trying to make large metal parts that are entirely a single crystal. They have succeeded with the white-hot blades of jet engines. If they could make a single-crystal wing it could be several times bigger than anything flying today, and still be made thinner, lighter, and more efficient. So far the biggest airplane is the An-225 six-engined freighter, built at Kiev in the Ukraine. It can take off weighing 1,322,750 lb (600 tons) – that is, twice as heavy as a 747 – and carry a cargo load of 551,150 lb (250 tons).

Such airplanes need huge airports with runways up to three miles (nearly 5 km) long. Since 1960 many STOL (short take-off and landing) and even VTOL (vertical take-off and landing) air-

Below: Boeing's 777 is the world's largest twinjet. Right: The 777 is designed almost entirely on computer, eliminating the need for a prototype.

planes have been built, partly to link city centers and partly for military and naval use. Britain's Harrier jumpjet pioneered the concept of a multi-role fighter and attack airplane that can never be caught on its airfield because it can operate from a hidden clearing in a wood, from a village, or from the deck of a small warship. Today many designers are trying to build bigger supersonic jumpjets, but the only one flying is Russia's Yak-141.

Vertical takeoff and landing

Jumpjets are too noisy for city centers, but the tilt-rotor airplane could be important both to airlines and the military. Following Bell's XV-15 of 1977, which demonstrated the concept, Bell and Boeing have built a number of V-22 Ospreys. An Osprey is basically a twin-turboprop airplane with the 6,000-horsepower engines on the wingtips. Each drives a prop-rotor with a diameter of 38 ft (11.58 m). Tilted upwards, these act as helicopter rotors to lift the V-22 vertically off the ground. Then the pilot gradually pivots the engines and prop-rotors forward until they act like huge propellers, turning the V-22 into a 350 mph (560 km/h) airplane. In this regard, the tilt-rotor can do anything a helicopter can do but can also fly two to three times as fast and, for any given amount of fuel, fly two to three times as far.

Another new VTOL development is the Notar (no tail rotor) helicopter. McDonnell Douglas pioneered helicopters in which air is blown through slits along the tail boom instead of a noisy and potentially dangerous rotor at the tail. This generates the desired lateral force to counter the

Above: While vertical takeoff and landing is the latest development in military aircraft, NASA has been moving in the opposite direction – space shuttles land like aircraft, while the X-30 National Aerospace Plane (on a runway) takes off and lands like an airplane.
Left: The Northrop B-2 Stealth bomber, made almost entirely of carbon (graphite) and other radar-absorbent materials.

torque needed to drive the main rotor, and gives enhanced maneuverability with less noise. Among conventional helicopter manufacturers, Westland in England has developed an improved main rotor which enabled its Lynx helicopter to take the speed record in 1986 at over 249 mph (400 km/h).

Bigger and stealthier

Designers of the biggest jetliners are finding it difficult to fit them into the gates at the airports. When in 1990 Boeing launched the 777, the world's biggest twin-engined airplane, it announced it was arranging for the outer part of each wing to fold upwards, reducing the span from 199 ft 11 in (60.93 m) to 155 ft 2 in (47.29 m). This was to set at rest the minds of customers who were afraid the giant Boeing would be too wide to fit between

other parked airplanes; altering the world's airports to accommodate the new airplane would cost many billions, so that was not a viable option. Eventually it was remembered that over 1,000 Boeing 747 "Jumbo Jets" are currently being operated with a span up to 211 ft 5 in (64.44 m), so the 777 may well not have folding wings by the time deliveries start in mid-1995. In any case all the big jetliner builders are busy trying to launch a Mega-carrier (so-called because of its weight of over 1,000,000 lb) with a span considerably greater than 200 ft (61 m). Such an airplane would incorporate all of today's advanced technologies, but in the present economic climate it would not feature such advances as aerodynamic laminar flow.

In 1935 the Scottish inventor of radar, Robin Watson-Watt, suggested that military airplanes would in future be designed so that they were difficult to see on enemy radars. This advice was ignored for over 40 years; then low-observable "stealth" technology was reinvented as something highly secret. So far it has resulted in the Lockheed F-117A, which uses a strange technique of faceting, covering the exterior surface with flat panels at different angles, and the Northrop B-2 strategic bomber. The latter is an all-wing design (by chance with the same 172 ft (52.43 m) span as a Northrop all-wing bomber of 1945) with a completely smooth exterior designed by computers and made of radar-absorbent materials. Eventually, all warplanes will probably be stealth designs,

Above: The U.S. Defense Department has tried to cancel the V-22 VTOL twin-turboprop airplane, despite the importance of its new technology. Right: The latest aircraft to use a ducted fan is the British Brooklands Optica observation plane. The fan is in a circular duct behind the cockpit, making it quieter and safer than a conventional propeller.

even the transporters and tankers, with special radar-enhancing reflectors to help friendly planes and ground controllers.

Fashion is surprisingly important in aerospace. Whereas in 1960 the VTOL jet and the swing-wing (with left and right wings pivoted to spread out sideways for take-off and to sweep back like an arrowhead for supersonic speed) were all the rage, today neither is attracting much interest.

Instead of swing wings the latest fighters have fixed wings with powerful slats and flaps, which are usually controlled automatically so that the pilot can concentrate on fighting the enemy. Several new fighters have been fitted with canard foreplanes instead of rear horizontal stabilizers, but the latest USAF fighter, the Lockheed F-22A, has the traditional arrangement. Indeed, the F-22A will probably not even have the two-dimensional (rectangular instead of circular) engine nozzles which were fitted to the prototypes to give vectored (swivelling) thrust to get out of smaller airfields and out-maneuver enemy fighters.

New propulsion methods

Jet engines are by no means the ideal propulsion unit for all aircraft. All aircraft propulsion systems are in some way jet engines, however, in the sense that they generate their thrust by accelerating a jet of air or hot gas to the rear. For slow airplanes the propeller is the most efficient way of doing this, but it is noisy and potentially dangerous on the ground.

The ducted fan, a compromise between the propellor and the jet, is essentially a multi-blade propeller running inside a suitably profiled circular duct. Some are driven by a gas turbine, in which case they may be called a ducted prop-fan. Smaller examples are driven by ordinary piston engines. Their advantages are that they are much quieter than a propeller, they pose no danger to nearby personnel and, in the event of structural failure of the fan, the parts can be contained within the duct (whereas people have been killed by detached propeller blades).

The first aircraft in production with a ducted fan was the German RFB Fantrainer. Here the fan is in the rear fuselage, driven by an Allison turbine engine. A later airplane is the British Brooklands Optica observation airplane. This uses a 260-hp piston engine to drive a fan aligned with the wing behind the bug-eyed cockpit. It is uncannily quiet, making just a gentle hum.

The cost factor

A dominant factor in aerospace engineering today is cost, and many new technologies are lying dormant. Most of the recent advances in big jetliners have been made by the Airbus company in Europe.

Above: The Lockheed F-22A is the latest USAF fighter airplane.

Examples include replacing the two-place glass cockpit with ordinary instruments with multifunction color displays; using the horizontal stabilizer as a fuel tank to trim the airplane without drag (and also extend range); using electronic FBW (fly by wire) technology to fly the airplane by computers, enabling the replacement of heavy mechanical links which suffer friction and backlash; using composite materials in primary structures; providing crew and passengers with a communications center able to do anything from booking an onward flight at destination to doing computerized control of duty-free stocks; and providing sleeping accommodation for a spare crew on 18-hour flights. But special cruise flaps for higher efficiency, and riblets (tiny grooves like the skin of a shark) to reduce drag are not yet being incorporated.

Why not? It all boils down to the poor economic climate, which determines what new technologies can be put to use. A contributory factor in the case of GA (general aviation, which comprises everything except the military and the airlines) is American laws on product liability. Cessna and Piper, for example, used to build thousands of light airplanes every year. Today the need to insure against capricious legal claims would double the price, so they build nothing but big turboprops and twin-engine airplanes which can better absorb such extra costs. Both GA airplanes and engines are unlikely to use any new technology at all until the economic climate improves.

Aerospace medicine

Modern civilian air travel protects its passengers from what is otherwise a medically hostile environment. Aerospace medicine deals with all aspects of the ways in which flight affects the human body. For example, it includes the physical and mental stresses of flight, the diseases that affect a person's ability to fly, the physical and psychological fitness standards of aircrew, and the human-machine interface.

Two-person crews

With the enormous improvements in avionics within the past two decades, not only have the cockpits in modern commercial aircraft become highly sophisticated, but the third member of the flight deck crew has become largely redundant. Many new aircraft are therefore operated by two-person crews. Technology now takes care of many of the tasks that the flight crew once carried out. But there has been a corresponding increase in the amount of information that the remaining crew members have to monitor, so the actual workload has not gone down. Nevertheless, airline economics dictate that planes carry as few crew, commensurate with safety, as possible. To ensure that safety is not compromised, the FAA (Federal Aviation Administration) now requires that workload is formally assessed on the flight deck of all new aircraft before certification is granted.

Crash survivability

Commercial air travel is remarkably safe, but accidents still happen. Some of these, especially those that happen after landing or during takeoff, are survivable, yet continue to claim lives. In several recent accidents, passengers survived a crash landing but died from asphyxiation in the fire that followed when the aircraft was on the tarmac with rescue crews close at hand. These accidents have prompted international aviation authorities to look more closely at the composition of cabin furniture to avoid using smoke-producing materials, at the installation of fire warning and firefighting equipment, and at various ways of helping passengers to survive. Examples include smoke hoods for passenger use, and audio tone devices and floor-level lighting to guide passengers to exit doors should the smoke at eye level be too dense.

All of these improvements, however, assume that aircraft occupants are in a fit state to escape from their stricken aircraft. But evidence from some accidents suggests that people are prevented from leaving the aircraft, usually by severe injury, but sometimes by mild concussion, caused by weaknesses in aircraft seats and mountings.

Above: Modern agile fighter aircraft place greater strains on their crew during routine flying maneuvers – up to 9 G – than ever before.
Below: Mock-up of the European Fighter Aircraft, a joint British, Italian, German, and Spanish project, due to enter service in 1998.

Material strengthening would help in these situations, but the use of rearward-facing seats, such as those found in many military transporter aircraft, would greatly improve the chances of survival. Cost and passenger resistance are used as excuses for not making this important improvement in commercial aircraft.

Agile fighter aircraft

Military aircraft often subject their crews to enormous stresses. The next generation of fighter aircraft will operate routinely at extremes of sustained acceleration (G) and altitude never before encountered; the success of missions will depend on how well the aircrew are protected.

One particular concern is G-induced loss of consciousness (G-LOC), in which the pilot of an aircraft suddenly loses consciousness within seconds of experiencing high G. This is because agile aircraft can attain a high acceleration well before the traditional symptoms and signs of G exposure have a chance to warn the victim. Once it was realized that G-LOC was a cause of military aircraft accidents over the last decade, intensive research began. The crews of new fighter aircraft, such as the USAF's Advanced Tactical Fighter (ATF), will benefit from a technique known as Positive Pressure Breathing. In 1991, the latter was introduced to the USAF F16 Fighting Falcon squadrons as part of the Combat Edge program.

Positive Pressure Breathing delivers breathing gas at raised pressure, and works by assisting the pilot's respiratory effort, thus reducing fatigue associated with repeatedly pulling G during air combat.

New breathing devices

Until recently, liquid oxygen provided the main source of breathing gas in military aircraft. Gas cylinders, the other alternative, are too heavy and too bulky. Now, new devices called molecular sieve oxygen concentrators, supplied by compressed air from the engines, are used in fighter aircraft such as the USMC AV8B, and will be used in the ATF.

Molecular sieves consist of beds of synthetic zeolites (hydrous aluminum silicates). Zeolites have the unique ability, under specific conditions of pressure and temperature, to alter their structure and selectively attract certain molecules, while allowing others to pass freely.

When air is delivered under pressure to beds of suitable molecular sieve material, nitrogen is selectively adsorbed onto the sieve, while oxygen passes through to the user. On reducing the pressure, the sieve releases the nitrogen, which is then flushed away. In Pressure Swing Adsorption, two beds are alternately pressurized to concentrate oxygen, and then depressurized to flush nitrogen. This produces a continuous supply of oxygen.

Molecular sieves are the ideal answer to the need for on-board delivery of oxygen to crews of small fighter aircraft where weight and space are at a premium. They are also useful in clinical medicine. Large units can supply the oxygen needs of whole wards, or even hospitals. And smaller, mobile versions can assist people with chronic lung disorders.

Above: This Boeing 737 crashed almost intact, but many lives were lost in the subsequent fire as passengers could not find the exits or were asphyxiated. This disaster, at Manchester Airport in 1985, prompted airlines to introduce new safety measures such as floor lighting.
Below: New instrumentation, shown here on the simulators of an Airbus A320, means that fewer crew are needed on the flight deck, requiring greater concentration.

Agricultural science

The chief goals of agricultural research have always been to increase yields and reduce the farmer's costs. In the 1950s and 60s these goals were met by the introduction of hybrid seeds, mechanization, and chemical pesticides that deprived insects and disease organisms of their share of the crops. In the 1980s and 90s the new tools of BIOTECHNOLOGY are being brought to bear, creating plants and animals tailored to provide higher yields and resist disease.

Drugs manufactured by bioengineered bacteria are already in use to improve the health of domestic animals. Meanwhile, organisms that cause disease in insects are being bioengineered to do an even better job, so they can replace chemical pesticides. Growth hormones manufactured by biotechnology cause cows to give more milk, and raise hogs with leaner meat.

One high-tech tool, artificial insemination, has been in widespread use since the 1950s, making it possible to spread the benefits of animal breeding programs quickly throughout the industry. About 75 per cent of dairy cattle in the United States are produced by artificial insemination. In addition to improving the quality of herds, the technique has reduced costs for many farmers, who no longer have to maintain their own bulls.

New technologies promise to increase the number of calves produced by the best cows, as well as the best bulls. These cows may be treated with hormones that stimulate the ovary to release up to six eggs per cycle, producing three or four embryos. The embryos are removed and implanted in "surrogate mothers," and the superior cow can be inseminated again in about three weeks.

The next step, still in the laboratory stage, is to allow the fertilized ovum to divide a few times, until the embryo consists of perhaps 32 cells, that is, after five divisions. The nucleus of each of these cells can be inserted into an egg from which the nucleus has been removed; that egg will develop into an embryo almost identical to the original. After a very few divisions this process no longer works, because cells in the embryo begin to differentiate to form specific parts of the animal. Researchers now are trying to learn more about how differentiation takes place so they can forestall it, to produce many offspring from one egg.

Modifying farm animals

Even the best animals can still be improved. Although terms like GENETIC ENGINEERING and "gene-splicing" sound futuristic and, to some, even disturbing, the fact is that plant and animal breeders have been moving genes around for centuries, using conventional techniques of crossbreeding and selection. But it will soon be common practice simply to insert the genes for desirable characteristics such as disease resistance or higher milk production.

One way to do this is to remove an ovum from an animal just after fertilization, then, under a microscope, inject DNA containing genes for the

Left: An assortment of genetic varieties (hybrids) of corn produced for experimental cultivation. Different strains display variation in thickness, length, and color of the cob, and the number of grains on the cob. Crossbreeding such varieties can produce new strains with chosen features.

Left: These potato chips were made from potatoes genetically engineered to improve their solids content. When fried, they absorb less oil, so they have fewer calories. They may be on sale by the end of the 1990s

Right: The cotton plants at left are genetically altered to resist bromoxynil herbicide. An unmodified plant at right, however, is damaged by the weedkiller.

Above: Open field trials of genetically engineered plants – here, oilseed rape – are already taking place despite some fears that "artificial" genes may spread.

desired characteristics directly into the nucleus with a tiny needle. The egg is then reimplanted in a surrogate mother. This method is still unreliable: several hundred modified eggs may be needed to produce one animal in which the inserted gene is "expressed" – that is, manufactures the protein for which it codes – and not all of the animals in which the gene is expressed may pass the trait on to their offspring.

This technique has been widely used in laboratory animals such as mice and rats, but it is still very difficult and expensive to apply to larger farm animals. A few genetically modified or "transgenic" farm animals have been created experimentally, although by 1992 none had yet been used in commercial farming. For example, pigs with an added gene for pig growth hormone grow faster and produce leaner meat. However, they are also subject to colds and arthritis, apparently resulting from the stress of rapid growth. Before leaner pigs can be engineered for commercial use further research is needed to understand the metabolic pathways by which fat is stored.

Green genes

An animal's egg cell can be removed from the body and is large enough to manipulate under a microscope. The egg cell of a plant is often far smaller, and is hidden inside the flower. Therefore, plant scientists often perform their genetic modifications on small pieces of plant tissue, such as a section of a leaf, or on plant cells growing in culture.

A favorite method for inserting genes into plant tissue uses a bacterium that causes a plant disease called crown gall. This bacterium infects a plant cell by inserting a ring of DNA called a plasmid into the cell. If the foreign DNA is linked into the plasmid it may be taken up and expressed by the plant cell.

Another method, developed by Dr. John Sanford at the New York State Agricultural Experiment

Station in Geneva, New York, is to attach the new DNA to tiny particles of gold and shoot them into cells using a patented "gene gun."

After the gene is inserted a new plant must be grown from the bits of plant tissue or cells in culture. Regenerating plants in this way has been particularly difficult with important grains such as wheat and corn; a major goal of research over the past decade has been to develop reliable techniques for working with these plants. It is still more of an art than a science.

High-tech plant breeding

No gene-splicing technique is of any use unless the gene for a desirable characteristic has been identified; it is also more difficult when the trait is carried by multiple genes. Old-fashioned plant breed-ing, aided by by some high-tech innovations, there-fore, is still of major importance.

The basic tool of classic plant breeding is the cross and backcross. For example, a breed of corn that resists drought might be desired. The breeder might start by crossing a commercial variety of corn with a Mexican kind that grows in arid regions. The descendants of the cross that show drought resistance is "backcrossed" with the com-mercial variety. After many generations of selec-tion and backcrossing a plant that is almost identi-cal to the original corn may be produced, but with drought resistance added.

Mapping of the plant genome using Restriction Fragment Length Polymorphisms (RFLPs – see GENETICS) has provided plant breeders with a road map that greatly speeds their work. Genetic mark-ers can be used to identify quickly the plants that carry desired traits, and will show whether the trait is controlled by a single gene or by multiple genes on different chromosomes.

Mapping also narrows down the location of a desirable gene to a particular fragment of DNA on a particular chromosome. That fragment of DNA can then be broken into smaller fragments which are spliced into plants; by testing the plants for the desired trait it is eventually possible to narrow the search and find the gene, after which the pro-tein for which it codes may be identified.

Sometimes no plant can be found with the char-acteristic a breeder would like to add. If the char-acteristic can be found in a plant that is not too distantly related, plant cells in culture can be fused, producing a *chimera* such as the pomato, which is part potato and part tomato. Like mules, many such interspecies fusions are sterile, but some can serve as breeding stock.

There is also a way for breeders to make their own genes: plant cells in culture are exposed to radiation or to a chemical that causes mutations, then exposed to a stress such as a toxin produced by a disease organism. If a mutation exists in the culture that confers resistance to the toxin, cells with that mutation will survive and can be regen-erated into plants that carry the resistance.

Farmers as good neighbors

Other scientists are studying the larger systems by which farming relates to the world around it. Primitive farmers could move to a new field when the soil became exhausted, and their activities sel-dom had any effect on anyone outside their fields. As modern agriculture becomes more intense and specialized and space more limited, it becomes important to understand how chemicals interact with the soil, and where they may go from there.

For instance, many dairy farmers no longer grow all their own feed, but buy some of it from

Antisense/UC82B Fruit:
Three weeks post harvest

Control UC82B Fruit:
Three weeks post harvest

Left: The tomato is a plant of great economic value. Here, genetically modified fruits, on the left, are compared with unmodified tomatoes three weeks after harvesting. The engineered tomatoes have greatly improved shelf life.

distant suppliers. As a result they can no longer dispose of the manure produced by their cattle by spreading it on their grazing land as fertilizer; they may not own enough land in proportion to the size of their herds. So they either overspread the manure, applying more than growing things can use, or dump it into holding ponds. Like chemical fertilizer, manure releases nitrates into ground water. If these reach public water supplies they can cause widespread disease; in lakes and streams they may cause a blooming of water plants that interferes with, and ultimately kills, fish and other wildlife.

A more familiar example is the ongoing effort to reduce the use of chemical pesticides. Some growers have traditionally applied pesticides "preventively," with the result that they sometimes applied chemicals that weren't needed. But using methods such as Integrated Crop Management (see AGRONOMY) fields are carefully monitored and pesticides applied only when insects appear in dangerous numbers (or ideally, just before that time).

The computer has become an essential tool in studying systems like these. Soil scientists are developing computer simulations to predict how nitrates, pesticides, and other materials will move through the soil, taking into account the structure and density of the soil and how rapidly it "biodegrades" chemicals.

Eventually scientists hope that a better understanding of the relationship between farming and the environment will lead to a "sustainable" agriculture that preserves soil and water quality, while needing a lower input of fertilizer, pesticides, and other chemicals. Such a system would reduce the farmer's costs while protecting the environment.

• FACT FILE •

- In order to manipulate plants and animals in useful ways, scientists must understand how they really work. More and more the emphasis in research has shifted from field testing to basic studies of the physiology of plants and animals, and of the pests and diseases that afflict them. This basic research often yields practical results.

- Mexican researchers studying *Pseudomonas syringae*, a bacterium that causes a disease in beans, have discovered that it carries a gene that deactivates its own toxin. When they inserted that gene into tobacco plants they found that the plants became resistant to the disease. (Tobacco, a much-studied plant, serves plant scientists as a sort of laboratory mouse.)

- Many insects attract potential mates by releasing into the air chemicals called pheromones. After learning the chemical composition of some sex pheromones and how they influence mating behavior, scientists have used them either to attract insects to traps or simply to confuse the timing of their mating cycle, thereby providing pest control without poisonous chemicals.

- A major problem for produce marketers is the premature ripening and softening of fruits en route to market. Workers at the New York State Agricultural Experiment Station in Geneva have traced this process to the action of an enzyme, polygalacturonase, which softens cell walls, and developed a method to block the action of the gene that codes for the enzyme. They are now studying the biochemical processes that cause the gene to be turned on in the first place.

Agronomy

Farmers the world over are agronomists. As overseers of land they try to manipulate the soil and various inputs to achieve a desired end, usually the production of food, fiber, and forage. The science of agronomy is concerned with the productivity of the soil.

Agronomy is inevitably driven by the need for cost effective production. Here, plant breeding plays a key role. By offering growers seeds with potentially better yields, breeders spread the expense of labor and machinery, as well as direct inputs such as fertilizers and weedkillers.

The genetic make up of plants lies at the heart of many modern developments (see AGRICULTURAL SCIENCE and BOTANY). Scientists have a growing understanding of the way genes work and how they interact to allow crops to fend off pests and diseases. This helps greatly in choosing the best combinations of parent plants, and speeds up the complex crossings needed to obtain new varieties.

Genes also determine the nature of end products, whether it be flour from wheat or oils from brassica crops, such as cabbage. The prospects for bringing specific genes together in completely new ways are particularly exciting. By using methods that would rarely, if ever, occur in nature, breeders expect to produce "designer crops" to meet highly specific needs. Creations such as an apple-flavored potato may even be possible. Oilseeds in which the make-up of the extract has been adjusted to suit particular markets are well advanced. Farther off is the cereal which makes its own nitrogen fertilizer in the same way that legumes, such as beans and clover, do.

Agronomy is at the center of the debate over the use of GENETIC ENGINEERING. Many people maintain that the latest techniques for shifting genes from one plant to another are unnatural and should be avoided. But breeders usually counter that their processes merely hasten what might eventually occur anyway, or simply involve using natural material in new ways. Whatever the rights and wrongs, most advanced countries have strict laws governing such work and the release of novel organisms into the environment.

Pinpointing need

While genetic engineering is one hot topic, concern for the environment is another. Quite apart from the financial implications there is a growing awareness of the need to use agrochemicals with care. Agronomists are keen to avoid repeating the story of DDT, a valuable insecticide with unfortunate long-term side effects on some bird life.

Forecasting diseases and diagnosing them before they become apparent to the naked eye are two areas attracting a great deal of research. The idea is that prevention or cure then needs fewer chemicals. The same principles apply to controlling pests. Hitting them when they are most vulnerable means using less pesticide.

An example of this type of work is being carried out at Bristol in the U.K. Researchers there have

Far left: This splashmeter can help farmers control leaf blotch disease by showing when dye in the dishes is splashed to leaf height. Fungicide can then be applied only when rain conditions require it, saving both spraying costs and environmental damage. Left: In an experiment to investigate the feeding patterns of natural predators of crop pests, biologists set up these mini-tents to provide a controlled environment. The aim is to use natural controls in place of heavy chemical application.

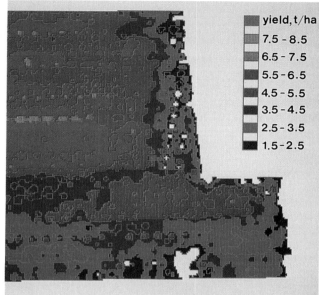

yield, t/ha

7.5 - 8.5
6.5 - 7.5
5.5 - 6.5
4.5 - 5.5
3.5 - 4.5
2.5 - 3.5
1.5 - 2.5

developed a disease-monitoring tool called a splashmeter. Consisting of a ring of dishes containing a dye solution and a central column of recording paper, it measures the intensity of rain falling on wheat crops.

Bouncing rain drops spread the spores of the leaf blotch disease *Septoria tritici* to the upper parts of the plants. But not all rain has the same effect, and it can be difficult to judge when the critical level is reached. Knowing when a critical amount of splash occurs allows advisers to time fungicide sprays more precisely and so save the farmer money.

Many diseases, pests, and weeds are now becoming resistant to the chemicals which are applied to control them. Until quite recently, weeds that had evolved resistance to herbicides were little more than curiosities, but now about 100 species have strains able to shrug off our best weaponry against them. One way to overcome this is to vary the approach used frequently, as pests which have genetic resistance to one chemical may be susceptible to another or to biological controls. Such tactics have acquired the title Integrated Crop Management. At Southampton University, England, one such idea involves creating specially sown grass ridges within cereal fields. Scientists have found these so-called "beetle banks" form a warm over-winter habitat for the many insects which in spring and summer prey on aphids attacking the crop.

More futuristic, but already beyond the drawing board stage, is the use of computers and orbiting satellites to help pinpoint precise field treatments. Grain harvesters fitted with global-positioning and yield-monitoring equipment can record crop out-

Above left and above: Total crop management in action. This aerial view of a barley field shows weed patches. Such data recorded over time is used to control an automatic sprayer, so chemicals are applied only where needed. Sensors on the harvester provide a map of the yield from the same area (above) so that the long-term effects of spraying and other inputs can be monitored.

put as it varies in each part of the field. The data can then be fed to computer-controlled fertilizer and spraying machines working over subsequent crops. This should allow nutrient deficiencies and weeds to be tackled only where strictly needed.

To till or not to till?
Soil tillage is an important topic in agronomy. Despite the advent of herbicides the traditional moldboard or self-scouring plow remains the basic cultivation tool for many farming systems. However, in many parts of the world, growers, soil scientists, and machinery makers are exploring other ways of preparing the land for sowing crops.

Inverting large volumes of soil each season is expensive, and many soil scientists believe that it actually reduces soil quality. Much effort is put into checking the quantity of organic matter in the soil. If this is increasing, so is the soil quality.

So-called no-till or direct drilling, in which seeds are sown straight into the land cleared of the previous crop, has attracted much attention in recent years. The technique requires specially designed machinery and relies heavily on good soil structure and pesticides for its success. But in the right area, it can improve the soil's water intake, improve its structure, and reduce erosion.

Anatomy and surgery

The science of anatomy underwent a wave of advances in the 1960s and 70s with the introduction of electron microscopes, which made it possible to examine the tissues of the body in detail. However, since then, this detailed understanding of anatomy has led to new, non-invasive methods of looking into the living human body. Ultrasound has become a standard technique for monitoring the growth, anatomy, and movement of fetuses, while CAT scans (*computerized axial tomography*, now renamed CT scans), developed in the 1960s, have improved in the quality of their images. Using numerous small-dose X-rays and a computer, they are an effective way of viewing "slices" of a living body.

New imaging techniques have been developed since the mid 1980s. In one scanning technique the patient takes, either by mouth or by intravenous injection, a radiochemical which is chosen to be taken up by the organ being tested. A radioisotope within the compound emits gamma rays which are imaged by a gamma camera. This camera is linked to a computer and is rotated around the patient so that the computer can construct an image of the slice, showing how much of the isotope has been taken up. This can show areas of abnormal metabolism, output, blood flow, and transit time. This is called *emission computerized axial tomography* (ECAT) or sometimes *single photon emission computerized tomography* (SPECT).

The technique of positron emission tomography (PET scanning) also produces an image of a previously administered radioisotope in large organs such as the brain. For example, to study oxygen utilization the oxygen isotope $_{15}O$ is mixed with the air the patient breathes. An array of detectors records positrons so that a computer can reconstruct an image on the screen. Other isotopes used are $_{13}N$ and $_{11}C$. All have a short half-life of between 2 and 20 minutes, so they must be produced by an in-house cyclotron.

Magnetic resonance imaging (MRI), formerly called nuclear magnetic resonance (NMR), is based on the fact that some atoms, notably hydrogen, behave as small magnets. Their axes of spin, normally random, become aligned if they are subjected to a strong magnetic field. By disturbing this field with another field at 90° the molecules realign and their energy levels change. These can be measured, depicting a "slice" of the body which highlights any abnormalities.

All of these images can be digitized and stored indefinitely in computer memory. Digital X-rays are also available and are used where the radiologist wants to subtract one image from another; for example, by subtracting the bones of the lower abdomen when imaging the flow of urine from the kidney to the bladder.

Endoscopy

Endoscopy is a generic name for various similar forms of viewing inside the body. A typical *endoscope* consists of a tube 10 mm in diameter containing a light, with optical fibers attached to a video camera and a pipe that blows carbon dioxide to separate the organs and allow a better view. Other optional facilities include tiny metal jaws to grasp hold of a piece of tissue, and a laser beam that can accurately destroy the most minute piece of diseased tissue while leaving the surrounding healthy tissue intact. Specialized forms of endoscope include the *gastroscope*, for viewing the gullet,

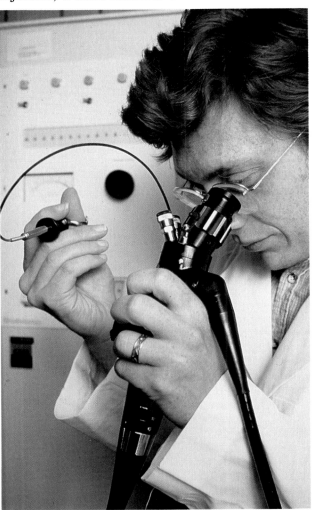

Left: A physician manipulates a remote-controlled fiber-optic endoscope. The tube of the flexible endoscope carries fiber optics for lighting and imaging plus several control cables and supply pipes.

Right and inset: A patient undergoing an MRI brain scan lies inside the coils of the machine in the background. This technique is particularly useful in resolving the nervous tissue of the brain. An image of the patient's brain and spinal cord appears on the screen in the foreground.

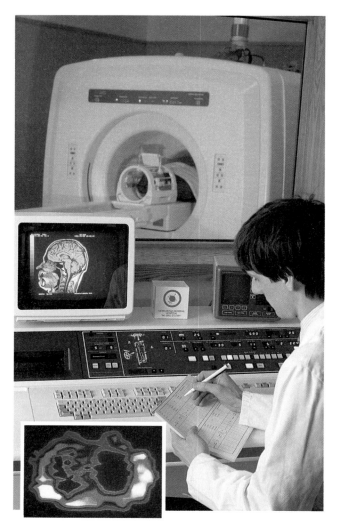

stomach, and duodenum; the *bronchoscope*, for viewing the lungs; the *proctoscope*, for viewing the rectum and colon; and the *laparoscope*, for viewing inside the abdomen. Laparoscopes used on babies and children are less than ¼ in. (5 mm) in diameter.

In a typical laparoscopic operation, such as gall bladder removal, the surgeon first makes four tiny punctures in the abdomen. An illuminated laparoscope is inserted through one hole, and instruments through another. The gall bladder is clamped off at both ends with clips inserted down a tubular instrument, a cautery is used to seal off any bleeding, and the gall bladder with its stone is removed though the largest hole, where the laparoscope went. Before this innovation was introduced in 1987, surgeons needed to make a long incision, and the patient had to stay in the hospital 9-10 days instead of 1-2 days, for the wound to heal.

Robot control

During laparoscopy, it is the task of an assisting doctor to point the laparoscope itself while the surgeon carries out the operation. A new development, however, involves a robotized pointing system. Tiny sensors on a headband pick up any movements of the surgeon's head.

Instead of instructing the assisting doctor how to move the camera, the surgeon simply makes natural movements of the head while watching a TV screen. The laparoscope moves accordingly, as if it were the surgeon's eyes.

Eventually, robots may actually wield the surgical instruments themselves, either under the control of the surgeon while watching an endoscope or

Right: The PET scan, by contrast, shows the takeup of a radio isotope within the brain cells. This is useful in measuring, for example, oxygen usage in patients with such disorders as senile dementia and brain tumors.

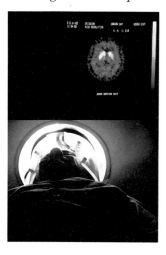

scan image, or automatically on a chosen route into the patient. The first use of such a system, using a device called "Robodoc" took place in 1992.

Endoscopes are also used to operate inside joints, and to repair hernias and remove kidneys and uteruses. Organs such as kidneys are encased in a strong plastic bag and macerated into small pieces so that they can be removed through the hole made for the endoscope. In theory, almost any operation except a transplant can be done endoscopically; it may even be possible to avoid heart bypass surgery by using an endoscope and a laser to drill tiny holes in the heart muscle so that it gets oxygen as it pumps blood.

The medical use of lasers has brought further advances in surgery. Lasers are used to drill tiny holes in the iris of the eye to relieve the pressure of glaucoma, to burn away precancerous cells of the cervix, to remove tattoos and birthmarks, and, more controversially, to alter the shape of the cornea to correct nearsightedness and astigmatism (see OPHTHALMOLOGY).

Aquaculture

Aquaculture is the farming of fish, mollusks, and crustaceans, which are stocked, fed, and protected much as livestock is on land. The cultured animals are in individual or corporate ownership; aquaculture is therefore sharply distinguished from the traditional "capture" fisheries. Although aquaculture has a long history, it was only in the 1980s that scientific and technical advances began to boost production. The world fisheries catch is approaching 100 million tons, while world production of cultivated fish was 9.3 million tons in 1990 – double that of 1983. In the same period crustacean culture increased fivefold to 789,000 tons.

Aquaculture now accounts for more than half of world production of freshwater and brackish-water fish. These are predominantly various species of carp, tilapia, and milkfish, reared in traditional fishponds in Asia for local consumption at low cost. By contrast, Japan, U.S., and Europe rear salmon, trout, and catfish, and marine fish such as yellowtail and sea bream in intensive systems for diversified and distant markets.

New technologies to supply seed
Aquaculture relies increasingly on artificially propagating eggs and "seed", or fry (recently hatched fish), rather than collecting wild fry, the supply of which is both limited and seasonal. The aim is to control the sexual cycle of the fish, which include species of carp, catfish, and marine fish. This is now largely done with injections of modern synthetic hormones, which are more reliable than traditional pituitary extracts.

Trout, sea bass, and turbot are controlled by alternating light and darkness to simulate the changes of the seasons and trick the fishes' "biological clocks" into advancing or delaying spawning. Many hatcheries maintain several separate broodstocks with different "day" and "night" patterns to ensure year-round egg supplies.

Fish sperm can be preserved as a gene bank for several weeks at 25° F (-4° C) and can be preserved indefinitely in liquid nitrogen at -321° F (-196° C). In the case of salmon or trout it is now commonplace to manipulate the chromosome number. To do this, eggs are subjected to heat or pressure soon after fertilization, which results in triplets of chromosomes rather than the usual pairs. These fish grow rapidly to market size, but do not become sexually mature and cannot interbreed with wild populations. By using sperm that have been treated with ultraviolet light, only the female chromosomes are active and all the offspring are genetically identical. This is a valuable tool for GENETIC ENGINEERING.

Above: Fish fry used in aquaculture tend to be raised artificially, often using hormones and genetic engineering to produce the required quality of stock. These fry are from a factory in Java, Indonesia.

Below: Shrimps are among the most common of farmed fish; production from farms such as this in Ecuador increased dramatically during the past decade.

Advances in feeding

Much of the recent expansion in marine fish and shrimp culture has been triggered by the development of improved feeds in the form of suitable live plankton and "microencapsulated" food pellets. Many hatcheries enrich these foods with HUFA (higher unsaturated fatty acids), derived from fish or squid oil, which is vital for normal development.

Fish require approximately 30-50 per cent animal protein in their diet. Aquaculture consumes one seventh of the world's fish meal; this may ultimately limit production from intensive aquaculture unless cost-effective substitute protein sources are developed.

New dietary formulations have a higher energy content and have more digestible proteins and carbohydrates, which minimize the production of feces and pollution from the animals' wastes. Modern extrusion and expansion processes yield food pellets that do not break up so readily in water and are designed to have the right buoyancy: bottom-dwelling fish such as turbot will eat pellets that sink to the bottom, while salmon, for example, prefer slow-sinking pellets.

Moving to deeper waters

Most marine fishes are reared in cages in sheltered inshore sites. Further expansion depends on moving farther offshore, where there is better water quality and waste dispersal, and where nets can be larger and deeper. These will mean that the fish do not have to be stocked as densely, resulting in less disease and faster growth. But offshore systems need to be stronger to withstand the wind and waves. Some nets enclose nearly a million cubic feet (25,000 cubic meters) of water and 400 tons of fish. Possible alternatives to nets are "curtains" of air bubbles or of cold water, pumped from the depths and allowed to descend around the enclosed area. The latter technique is presently being tested with tuna, which do not like to enter cold water.

Disease control

In 1991 more than one in three Scottish salmon died from disease, mainly caused by bacteria and parasitic sea lice. Bacterial and viral epidemics have caused serious losses of marine shrimp. Antibiotics are increasingly used against bacteria, but the appearance of drug resistance, and even cross-resistance to more than one drug, calls for a wider range of measures.

One alternative is to use vaccines. The problem of injecting large numbers of fish has led to the development of oral vaccines against the major diseases of salmon and catfish.

In the past, sea lice have been controlled with organophosphate pesticides, but these threaten

Above: A salmon farm in Scotland. Scottish salmon farms have suffered greatly from disease throughout the 1990s.
Below: A typical salmon farming net seen from underwater in Norway.

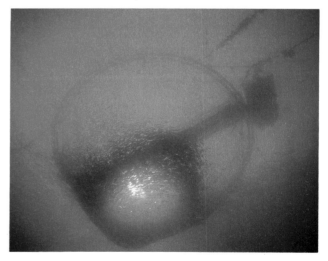

the survival of marine life and have become less effective as resistance has developed. Alternative natural compounds are under test – one from a fungus, another from a chrysanthemum. Biological control with wrasse, fish that are natural "cleaners", looks promising.

The best method of disease control is good husbandry: ensuring good water quality, preventing excessive densities of stock, and avoiding feed wastage. Marine farms increasingly rotate their sites and allow each to lie fallow for a season, to give it a chance to recover from the pollution and parasites that will inevitably have built up. Neighboring enterprises synchronize their disease treatments to avoid a cycle of reinfection.

Archaeology

Archaeology is the study of the human past from its material remains. These remains range from fragile traces of campsites nearly two million years old in East Africa, or early villages in the Near East where the first farmers lived, to more recent historical settlements such as the colonial town of Williamsburg in Virginia.

While modern archaeology is not a science itself, it utilizes many recently developed scientific methods to help find, excavate, and analyze material from ancient sites.

Discovering sites

The first stage in any archaeological investigation is to locate the sites where people once lived. Archaeologists are always on the lookout for traces of former human habitation in the landscape, from pieces of broken ceramics to coins. While many sites are still found by chance, numerous possible areas have now been surveyed. Rather than examine a whole area in minute detail, small areas are studied intensively either by looking for surface remains, or by digging sample trenches.

Techniques of STATISTICS then help archaeologists to work out the total number and distribution of sites. Samples of as little as 4 per cent of the total area have been used to draw conclusions about both the settlement patterns within a region and the internal structures of individual sites.

Aerial photography has been used for many years to look for such things as ancient earthworks. Although it is usually carried out from airplanes, these cannot really fly low enough; in recent years cameras have been hoisted aloft on tethered blimps or balloons and kites, using a radio signal to trigger the shutter.

Close-up views of buildings such as the Palace of Knossos in Crete allow every stone to be plotted on highly accurate plans. These are vertical views, but airplanes can also take oblique pictures which give better perspective and place a site in its environmental context.

At the other extreme, satellite images can show vegetation differences through false-color imagery, thus revealing overgrown ruins. Equally useful is airborne radar, which penetrates vegetation, and thus is helpful in forested regions such as the tropics. It was used by NASA to map extensive networks of canal-like features in Belize and northern Guatemala. Some of these features were ancient Mayan drained fields, used for intensive agriculture, but others were natural joints in the bedrock. In Costa Rica ancient footpaths were found, documenting a web of communications several thousand years old.

Above: A magnetometer in use during the geophysical survey of a buried site in England, by the Ancient Monuments Laboratory of English Heritage. Below: A plot of magnetometer survey data, illustrating the discovery of an Iron Age settlement complex in Cornwall, England. The large enclosure is about 23 ft (70 m) across.

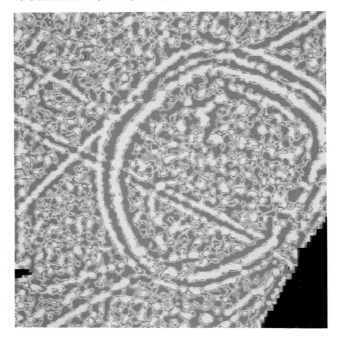

Mapping sites

Once an archaeological site has been pinpointed, both buried and surface features need to be plotted as accurately as possible before excavation begins. For many years, archaeologists have used such tools as resistivity meters, proton magnetometers, and metal detectors to build up a picture of the site. However, these archaeological tools are now being supplemented by a range of new techniques also used in GEOPHYSICS. For example, a subsurface radar scanner, mounted on a trolley and dragged across the site on transects, sends rapid pulses into the soil to a depth of 10 ft (3 m). Different echoes return from solid features such as walls, compared with softer ones such as grave fill.

Geo-radar equipment, mounted on a slow-moving vehicle, assesses time and energy differences between transmitted and reflected pulses to locate layers of contrasting density, while the seismic "standing wave technique" sends sound waves through the soil by striking it repeatedly and measuring the time that the waves take to reach a detector; they will move more slowly through soft deposits. This is similar to sonar, long used by ships as an echo-sounder to detect navigational hazards, and now by maritime archaeologists to find wrecks on the sea floor. Sonar has also been used on dry land to detect tombs in the Valley of the Kings in Egypt.

All of these methods measure anomalies or irregularities below ground. Natural features, as well as archaeological remains, will give signals, so it is necessary to define the general area of investigation as closely as possible.

New instruments have greatly speeded up mapping on the surface and in the excavation trenches. While the traditional plane table and alidade, or surveyor's level and staff, are still widely used, the electronics revolution has produced the electronic distance-measuring theodolite. In this, a standard optical telescope is used to locate the target staff, up to 1.24 miles (2 km) away, and then an ultrasound signal is sent to it and reflected by retroprisms attached to the staff. The distance can be measured to within a few centimeters, and the instrument can be set to display the horizontal and vertical angles.

Dating sites

Radiocarbon dating is still the most widely used scientific method of deciding on the age of an artifact. Carbon is present in all living things, and where it is preserved by burning, waterlogging, or desiccation it is one of the most common constituents of ancient structures, burial sites, and trash heaps. Measuring the rate of decay of the isotope carbon-14 yields the proportion of carbon-14 to the more common isotopes carbon-12 and

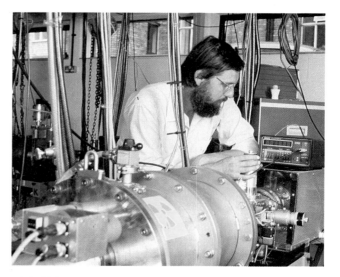

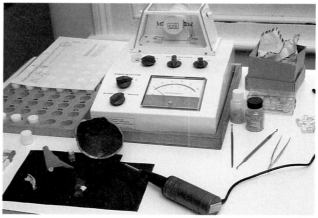

Above: Roman pottery being prepared for analysis by atomic absorption – one of the techniques used by scientists today to determine the elemental content of archaeological samples. Methods such as this have enabled archaeologists to identify the composition of ceramic containers used to transport goods and so build up maps of ancient trade routes.

carbon-13, which do not decay. From this, the age of the organic material can be calculated.

Radiocarbon dating has become more precise with the development of accelerator mass spectrometry (AMS): instead of counting the decay events of carbon-14, the numbers of atoms are counted directly and compared to those of the stable isotopes carbon-12 and carbon-13.

Because far smaller samples are needed with the AMS method, single seeds or tiny fragments of important objects can be dated. Among the results has been the exposure of the Turin Shroud as a fourteenth-century fake. In a less well-publicized investigation, it was discovered that cultivated barley found on a 17,000-year-old site at Wadi

Left: A purpose-built accelerator mass spectrometer at one of the leading archaeological dating laboratories in Oxford, U.K. The sample is ionized and the ion beam is separated into a spectrum of particles by means of an electric field.
Right: Maps produced by proton-induced X-ray emission show the elemental make-up of the handle of this 19th-century Iranian knife. Colors are used to illustrate variations in the elemental concentrations within each map (yellow denotes the highest concentration). The right column of maps show that the body of the handle consists of a steel alloy containing iron, and concentrations of nickel, chromium, and vanadium. The inlay is an alloy containing gold, silver, copper, and zinc.

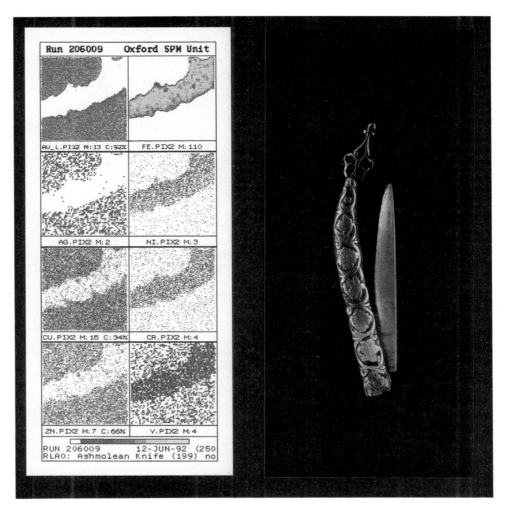

Kubbaniya in Egypt actually belonged to much later layers on the site. If, however, the older date had been confirmed, it would have meant that the practice of farming was almost twice as old as had originally been thought.

Dates have even been obtained from blood used as a binder in Pleistocene cave paintings in both Europe and Australia, while other analytical methods have been used to identify the source of the blood as human or otherwise.

Analyzing finds

One important archaeological technique is to establish exactly either where a particular artifact was made or where its materials originated. For example, thin sections of stone axes or Mayan jades can be placed by matching them with existing rock samples, and minerals in pottery can be used to help identify where trade wares come from. Neolithic ceramics were transported over 62 miles (100 km) before 3000 BC, while Roman amphorae were distributed all across the Empire.

While many materials have a basically similar composition, with the same major elements occurring everywhere, trace elements present only in a few parts per million often vary between one source and another. The volcanic glass obsidian has been successfully traced from many sources to its final destination in ancient trash heaps by several methods.

Neutron activation analysis uses slow neutrons in a reactor to excite the atoms in the sample and convert them to unstable isotopes, which emit gamma rays of a characteristic frequency as they decay, producing a series of lines in a spectrum. The intensity of each spectral line indicates how much of each element is present. Proton-induced X-ray emission (PIXE) produces similar results, using an accelerator instead of a nuclear reactor. X-ray fluorescence spectrometry uses a beam of X-rays to excite secondary X-rays in the sample, with wavelengths and energies indicating how much of each element is present.

The electron microprobe focuses a fine beam on a small area of the sample, again exciting electrons to emit characteristic X-rays. Atomic absorp-

Above: The analysis of DNA extracted from once-living tissue is becoming an important tool in archaeology. Just 2 g of this 17th-century bone will provide enough DNA to give genetic information about the ancestry of its former owner.

Below: Skeletal remains such as these in a medieval cemetery in England can now provide information on the background of the individuals. Tissue from up to 7000 years ago can be used, giving information on population movements.

tion spectrometry uses the principle that a material at high temperature will release light of a particular wavelength or color for each element present, which can be selected for by directing light of varying wavelengths through an acid solution of the sample sprayed in a flame.

In another method, known as inductively coupled plasma emission spectrometry (ICPS), the sample is excited in a plasma arc at much higher temperatures, with less overlap between the responses from each element.

These methods are accurate within 5 per cent; most results are plotted with a 95 per cent confidence limit. The particular combination and concentration of trace elements will characterize most sources of obsidian and other useful minerals such as flint or chert, enabling the archaeologist to make maps of ancient trade routes.

• FACT FILE •

- Most archaeological studies are concerned solely with the artifacts that people leave behind them. But occasionally, the people themselves are discovered, preserved in peat. For example, 168 bodies dating from around 5500 BC were found in peat near Titusville, Florida.

- Although the bodies are shrunken, the skin and internal organs are often present. It is even possible to investigate the stomach contents. In the case of the body of an Iron Age woman which was recovered from a peat bog in Djursland, Holland, in 1879, the remains had been kept in a museum for over a century before investigations were carried out.

- Using a medical technique, computerized tomography showed the position of food residues within the body; these were then removed with minimum damage by cutting a small opening in the abdominal wall. Her last meal had been of gruel made from rye.

- Skin taken from a male body found in a bog at Lindow, England, was examined using an electron probe X-ray microanalyzer. The results, published in 1990, implied that paints containing copper and zinc were present, presumably as part of body decoration. Further investigations may show whether the paint was applied in any sort of pattern.

Astrophysics

Of all the sciences, astronomy can claim to be the most comprehensive, covering the study of the universe as a whole. The difference between astronomy and astrophysics is becoming blurred, but astrophysics can be thought of as the branch of astronomy that applies physics to our understanding of the matter that makes up the universe. Astronomy also includes such topics as PLANETARY SCIENCE and COSMOLOGY.

As the end of the 20th century approaches, the great blossoming of astronomy over the past 50 years shows no sign of slowing down. The number of astronomers in the U.S. rose by 40 per cent in the 1980s to about 4200, with 2800 in active research. New revelations about the universe are constantly unfolding and new instruments guarantee more in the years ahead. U.S. astronomers are hailing the 1990s as the "Decade of Discovery" for good reason.

Astrophysics has been transformed in recent years by observations made from space using specially designed satellites. The best known, the Hubble Space Telescope, is now producing good results despite errors in the manufacture of its main mirror, which is 2.4 meters across (telescope mirror sizes are today quoted in meters rather than in inches). Although it is only one twentieth as sensitive as was hoped, astronomers have been able largely to compensate for the fuzzy optics by computer enhancement of the images. The telescope should be restored almost to full sensitivity when shuttle astronauts install correcting optics in 1993 or 1994.

Super-telescopes and CCDs

Space-borne telescopes, however, are expensive to build and operate, difficult or impossible to maintain and repair, and usually last only a few years. Apart from the 5-meter Hale Telescope on Palomar Mountain, California, and an ill-fated 6-meter in the Caucasus, until the early 1990s the largest ground-based telescopes were around 4 meters in diameter. Astronomers believe the time has come to strike out again and build a new generation of larger telescopes. Larger mirrors collect more light, enabling astronomers to peer much deeper into space.

Right: Modern ground-based telescopes rarely have tubes – a skeleton framework holds the optics. In the Keck Telescope on Hawaii, the world's largest, the main mirror consists of 36 individual segments. The optical design is otherwise similar to the HST, with a secondary mirror directing the light through a hole in the center of the main mirror to instruments behind it.

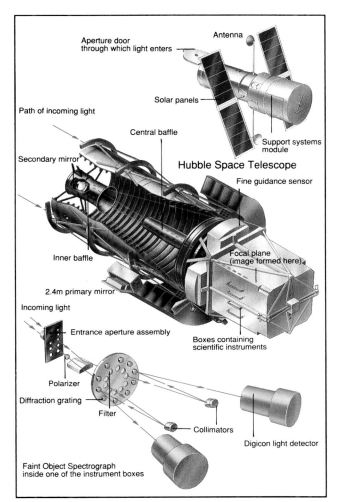

Above: The 2.4 meter mirror of the Hubble Space Telescope (HST) collects light from distant objects and reflects it to a central focus via a secondary mirror. The Faint Object Spectrograph, one of six main instruments, uses a diffraction grating to split the light for analysis.

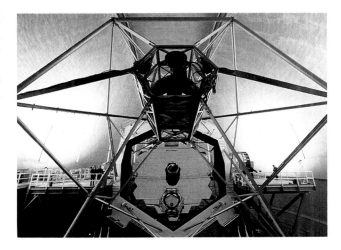

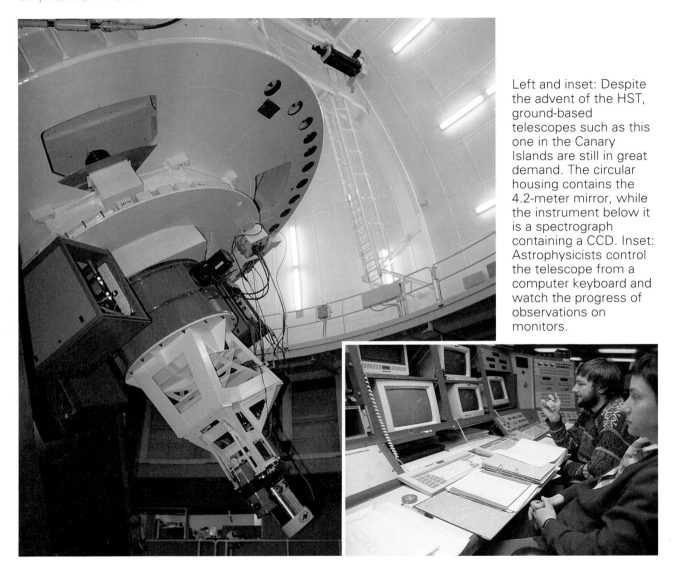

Left and inset: Despite the advent of the HST, ground-based telescopes such as this one in the Canary Islands are still in great demand. The circular housing contains the 4.2-meter mirror, while the instrument below it is a spectrograph containing a CCD. Inset: Astrophysicists control the telescope from a computer keyboard and watch the progress of observations on monitors.

Another advance has come from the widespread use of CCDs – charge-coupled devices. These are super-sensitive versions of the image detectors found in modern home video cameras. Their performance is improved by operating them at temperatures around –95° F (–70° C), provided by liquid nitrogen. One great advantage of CCDs over photography is that the data can be handled digitally and processed by computer software, thus enabling the images to be enhanced to bring out the greatest information.

One problem with siting telescopes on the ground rather than in space is that Earth's turbulent atmosphere smears out the images, reducing the fine detail that can be seen. But using "active optics", the shape of the mirror is continuously adjusted to compensate for the shimmering atmosphere. The new big telescopes will employ active optics to make images of stars being born out of dust clouds and of planetary systems forming around them.

The first of the super-telescopes, the Keck Telescope, was completed in April 1992 and began routine operation in 1993. Its primary mirror is made up of 36 hexagonal "segments", each ground and polished separately before being assembled into a large mirror with an effective diameter of 9.82 m. Keck is situated 14,000 ft (4200 m) above sea level on Mauna Kea, a dormant Hawaiian volcano which is rapidly becoming the world's leading astronomical observatory. A second 10-meter telescope, the Keck II, should be ready in 1996.

The European Southern Observatory, a consortium of European states, has a different approach to super-telescopes. Their $225 million Very Large Telescope (VLT) will be an array of four 8.2-meter telescopes that can work either independently or else linked to act as a single giant telescope. The

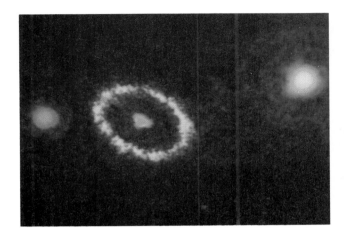

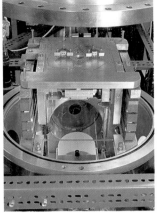

Left: The world's most sensitive gravity-wave detector, at Glasgow University, with arms just 30 ft (10 m) long, is to be superseded by detectors in the U.S. with arms 2.48 miles (4 km) long.

Above: This doughnut-shaped object at the center of a nearby galaxy, observed by the HST in 1992, is believed to be evidence for a black hole. The disk of cold gas and dust could be fueling a black hole with a mass 10 million times that of the Sun. At the disk's center, a bright spot shows where gravity is compressing and heating the material.

VLT is being built on the mountain of Cerro Paranal in the Chilean Andes. Meanwhile, many other groups in the U.S. and overseas, often in international partnerships, are working on plans for telescopes in the 8-meter class.

Cosmic questions

Since the early 1980s astronomers have discovered that clusters of galaxies are not distributed uniformly through the universe, but are arrayed on vast web-like structures with apparent voids between them. Noone knows why the universe is like this. Bigger telescopes will help astronomers survey deeper swathes of the universe to map these structures in greater detail.

Another question is the nature of the "missing mass": material which appears to pervade galaxies and galaxy clusters, and is revealed by its effects on their movements through space, yet is not visible. It may consist of perfectly ordinary dark bodies, such as cold planets, but so far these have failed to show up in other ways. Astrophysicists are wondering if more exotic explanations are called for. Only by continued observations of all types of objects will such problems be solved.

Research in astrophysics usually consists of making large numbers of observations of stars, galaxies, and the many other objects that fill the universe. In general, advances are made slowly as information is pieced together, building up a general picture of the way the universe works. Quite often, what may seem to be academic investigations into the structure or movement of distant objects can alter our understanding of more imme-

diate concerns, such as ENERGY PRODUCTION or PARTICLE PHYSICS. But occasionally an event occurs which provides a wealth of new data and transforms our knowledge. Such an event was the explosion of supernova 1987A.

The death of a star

On February 23rd, 1987 a bright star suddenly flared into the southern sky. It was a supernova; not a new star but the death of an old one. Its appearance provided astrophysicists with a long-awaited glimpse of stardeath, and the observations made of the event provided a crucial test for many modern theories.

Although astronomers had seen many supernovae in distant galaxies, 1987A was the closest and most spectacular since Galileo first turned a telescope on the stars almost four centuries ago. The supernova occurred in the Large Magellanic Cloud, a small companion to our own galaxy, and only 170,000 light years away from us. The proximity allowed astronomers to make observations that have never before been possible.

The instant of collapse was signaled by a burst of neutrinos – tiny sub-atomic particles – that swept through the Earth on February 23rd and was picked up by detectors in Japan and the former Soviet Union. Such a burst is predicted by current theories of supernovae but this was the first time it had been observed.

In 1990 the Hubble Space Telescope revealed a circular ring surrounding the supernova at a distance of 1.4 light years (that is, about a third of the distance between the Sun and the nearest star). It seems that the ring consists of gas blown off from the star many thousands of years before the explosion but is only now being illuminated.

But what astronomers are waiting for most of all is a pulsar. These rapidly spinning neutron stars, emitting regular pulses of radio waves, are believed to be created in supernova explosions. Although there have been some false alarms, the

Right: Hubble's Faint Object Camera located a ring of material surrounding the 1987 supernova in the Large Magellanic Cloud. This ring is debris previously thrown off by the star, at center.

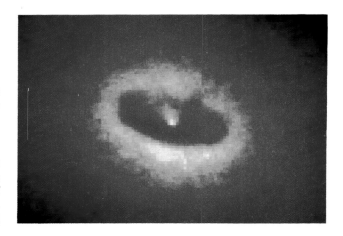

pulsar has yet to show itself, probably because it is still shielded by enveloping gas. When it finally appears many theories will be vindicated.

The search for gravitational waves
The waves of the electromagnetic spectrum are not the only carriers of information about the distant universe. Albert Einstein, in his General Theory of Relativity, predicted another class of waves – gravitational waves – that should be generated whenever a massive object is accelerated.

So far noone has definitely detected gravitational waves. They must be so weak that only catastrophic events on a cosmic scale, such as supernova explosions, colliding binary stars and pulsars, would be powerful enough to produce observable quantities of radiation.

The problem is to design a detector to sense them. The effect of a gravitational wave is to stretch and compress any objects through which it passes. But even the most violent cosmic events will produce fantastically small distortions of only one part in 10,000 million million million.

With the blessing of the National Science Foundation a team of scientists from the California Institute of Technology and the Massachusetts Institute of Technology are building two gravitational wave observatories, one in Hanford, Washington, and the other in Livingston, Louisiana. They will look nothing like conventional astronomical observatories. Each will consist of two metal tubes, 2.48 miles (4 km) in length, joined to form an L-shape. A weight will hang at the end of each arm of the L. A laser beam will be sent down each tube, reflected from mirrors on the weights, and the two beams brought back together to form an interference pattern. Any small changes in the lengths of the arms, such as those caused by a passing gravitational wave, will disturb the pattern and generate a signal.

Even with arms 4 km long, the detectors will need to sense movements thousands of times smaller than the size of an atomic nucleus. Scientists are confident that improved techniques of laser interferometry will do just that.

Similar projects are being planned in Europe, with German-British and Italian-French proposals at advanced stages, and an Australian-Japanese observatory is also being discussed. At least four widely spaced observatories will be needed, both to pinpoint the source of the waves and to convince astrophysicists that the detections are real and not caused by local interference.

• FACT FILE •

● Since the 1930s astrophysicists have known that the Sun is powered by nuclear fusion. Every second, over 600 million tons of hydrogen are converted into helium in searing heat and crushing pressure at the heart of the Sun. The fusion theory has been extremely successful in explaining how the Sun and other stars work and how they pass through their life cycles. But there is a problem.

● The only way to see what is happening in the center of the Sun is to observe the neutrinos that are created in the reactions. If our eyes were sensitive to neutrinos we would be able to see the nuclear reactions as an intensely bright spot in the middle of the Sun's disk. Astro-physicists can accurately predict how many neutrinos should be produced. If we could observe neutrinos we would have a powerful test of the fusion theory.

● Neutrinos are so elusive that it is very difficult to detect them. Nonetheless, four neutrino detectors are now running, in the U.S., Japan, Russia, and Italy. All four show that there are not enough neutrinos coming from the Sun. And astrophysicists are worried.

● More sensitive and powerful detectors are being planned in Japan and Canada. We shall have to wait another few years before we know for sure whether there is something wrong with our understanding of the Sun, with our understanding of neutrinos, or both.

Bacteriology

Bacteria are tiny single-celled organisms. Typically, 1000 cells laid side by side would measure only $\frac{1}{25}$ in. (1 mm). Although they contain DNA, this is not organized inside a nucleus as in other organisms. Mitochondria and chloroplasts, the "energy factories" of animal and plant cells, are also missing from bacteria. Indeed, there is now evidence that these structures probably evolved from bacteria. This is one of the exciting discoveries made possible by the advances in MOLECULAR BIOLOGY in the last few decades. These have enabled bacteriologists to understand and even modify the composition and behavior of bacteria in ways which would have seemed incredible only 20 years ago.

Many bacteria in the environment perform functions which are vital to us and all other higher life forms, including the decomposing of dead plant and animal matter and the "fixing" (incorporation into organic molecules) of atmospheric nitrogen. Some interesting new ways of using the ability of bacteria to decompose a great variety of compounds are currently being developed. One of the most important of these is spraying oil spills with mixtures of bacteria selected for their ability to degrade hydrocarbons. These bacteria are grown in vast quantities (several tons of cells) in laboratories.

This approach, known as bioremediation, was used with some success on the beaches of Prince William Sound in Alaska, following the 11 million gallon oil spill from the *Exxon Valdez* in 1989, and again following the 1990 Gulf War. Mixtures of bacteria capable of degrading toxic chemicals such as certain pesticides and herbicides are also being developed. The environment may also benefit from the introduction of biodegradable plastics which have been manufactured from insoluble polymers produced by some bacteria and readily decomposed by others.

People have employed bacteria in various industrial and agricultural processes for many centuries. Originally they were used unwittingly to produce various fermented food products. The dairy industry is notable for its wide use of bacteria, which are important in the production of cheese, yogurt, and some butters. Now that these processes are better understood by bacteriologists, they can be more closely controlled than was previously possible, giving a more reliable product.

The rapid growth and great biochemical versatility of bacteria make them extremely useful to biotechnologists who can now use bacterial cultures to manufacture products which would be too complex to be prepared by chemical means. Methods have been developed to greatly increase the quantities of the products which bacteria produce naturally. By introducing genes from other organisms by GENETIC ENGINEERING, they can now yield completely new compounds. These strategies have led to products as diverse as enzymes (proteinases) for biological washing powders, antibiotics to fight infection, and human insulin for the treatment of diabetes.

Bacteria in human health and disease

The human body is full of harmless bacteria. But a minority of external bacteria are capable of invading the body and causing disease. They have been responsible for some of the great scourges of

Left: Water of a lake discolored by blue green algae *Cyanophyceae*. The phenomenon is known as water bloom. It could be due to an unusual amount of sunshine, or to a surplus of phosphorus or nitrogen derived from human activities. Some species of *Cyanophyceae* liberate a toxin which is harmful to zooplankton, fish, aquatic birds, and human beings. Water bloom may also lead to eutrophication, the progressive consumption of oxygen in the water.

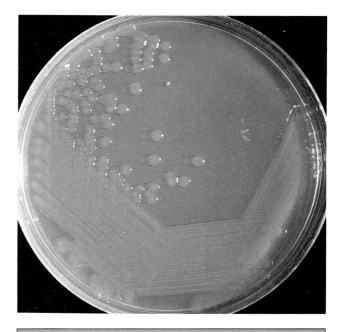

Left: *Vibrio cholerae*, the bacterial causal agent of cholera, growing on nutrient agar. Cholera is an acute epidemic disease which occurs mainly in countries lacking modern sanitary techniques. It is possible to be immunized against it.

humankind such as syphilis, tuberculosis, plague, cholera, and typhoid. With improved methods of diagnosis, such as the ability to locate and identify minute quantities of bacterial DNA by the polymerase chain reaction (see GENETIC ENGINEERING), it is likely that we will discover that many diseases for which no cause is currently recognized are, in fact, caused by bacteria. For example, in 1983 researchers first reported the association between bacteria (*Helicobacter*) and stomach ulcers. Such advances offer new hope in the treatment of disease.

Since the introduction of penicillin in the 1940s, antibiotics have greatly reduced the numbers of people dying or suffering disability from bacterial infections. However, many bacteria have developed resistance to antibiotics, particularly where they have been used indiscriminately. The search for new antibacterial agents continues in an attempt to combat the increase in resistance. Whereas the early antibiotics, such as penicillin, streptomycin, and chloramphenicol were produced by bacteria or fungi, many newer agents are synthesized by chemists, either in part (modification of existing antibiotics produced by microorganisms) or whole.

A range of completely synthetic antibacterial agents, the fluoroquinolones, introduced in the 1980s, have been very successful. Unfortunately, resistance to these agents is already appearing, so the battle with the continually adapting disease-causing bacteria continues.

• FACT FILE •

- The gold nuggets found in the silt of some riverbeds, which were responsible for several famed gold rushes, may have been produced by bacteria. This surprise observation was reported in 1992 by a scientist who examined thousands of grains of gold found in Alaska.

- Using a scanning electron microscope, which can magnify objects many thousandfold, bacteria were seen in close association with the grains of gold, which appeared to be deposited around channels occupied by the bacteria.

- The proposed mechanism of gold deposition is not alchemy, but a well recognized bacterial activity known as biomineralization. Several minerals are known to be precipitated by bacteria after concentration of dilute soluble salts found in the environment. Thus the bacteria would not be responsible for creating gold, but for concentrating it from soils rich in gold salts.

- Exactly how and why the bacteria perform this trick has still to be explained, but several investigators will no doubt attempt to repeat it in the laboratory with a view to commercial exploitation of these bacteria.

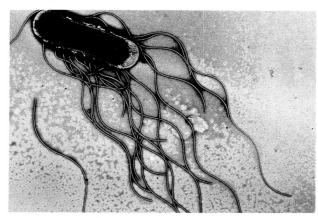

Above: Transmission electron micrograph (TEM) of the bacterium *Salmonella sp.*, a contaminant of food and a cause of food poisoning. The bacteria lodge in the intestines and multiply rapidly.

Biochemistry

Biochemistry can be simply defined as the science that deals with the chemistry of living organisms. Whether from a microbe or a human, it seeks to explain the properties of living organisms in terms of the chemical substances which they contain. Cells consist of extremely complex components: proteins, nucleic acids, carbohydrates, lipids (or fats), and a host of other smaller molecules, often present only in trace amounts. Moreover, thousands of chemical reactions are occurring in living cells simultaneously in a carefully controlled and regulated way. The outward manifestation of these reactions is life itself.

Living cells are separated from their environment by a membrane composed of a double layer of lipid. Embedded in this are a variety of membrane proteins which perform a variety of tasks. Some are selective channels for ions and solutes such as glucose, while others are part of the complex communication system between cells so characteristic of multicellular organisms. The messages are initially carried around the body in the form of small molecules, such as *ligands*, that diffuse through the intracellular medium and interact with larger molecules, such as proteins. For example, if a ligand such as a hormone interacts with a protein bound to the membrane (the hormone's *receptor*) that recognizes it, then a second intracellular messenger is generated. This in turn may lead to a change in the cell's metabolism. Two such second-messenger systems have been identified.

The first, *cyclic-AMP*, was discovered by Sutherland in 1972. It is formed from ATP – an all-purpose energy molecule – by the activation of an enzyme, *adenylate cyclase*, which is bound to the membrane. The cyclic-AMP then activates enzymes called *kinases* which in turn can transfer phosphate groups to key metabolic enzymes, switching them on or off as appropriate. The challenge has been to discover how the binding of a ligand to a receptor on the outer membrane of the cell activates the adenylate cyclase.

A powerful tool in working out this process has been the development of analogs which mimic the activity of the natural ligand, termed *agonists*, and others which block the activity of the natural ligand, termed *antagonists*. In fact, some of the most effective drugs for asthma, hypertension, and stomach ulcers work at their respective receptors

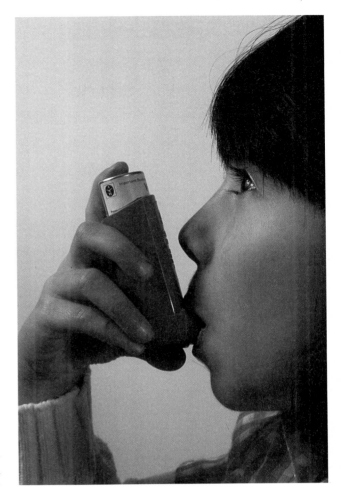

Above: A child uses an inhaler to take the drug salbutamol, which uses an agonist to activate the appropriate receptor to cause a dilation of the bronchial muscles in order to relieve asthma.

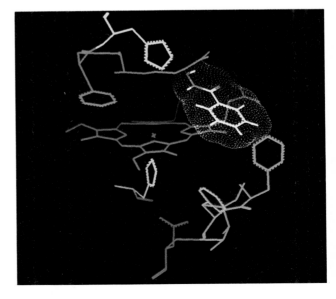

Right: Computer-generated structure showing how an aromatic ligand binds to a plant peroxidase enzyme. The biological activity of the enzyme is determined by the shape of the pocket into which the ligand molecule, shown stippled, fits exactly.

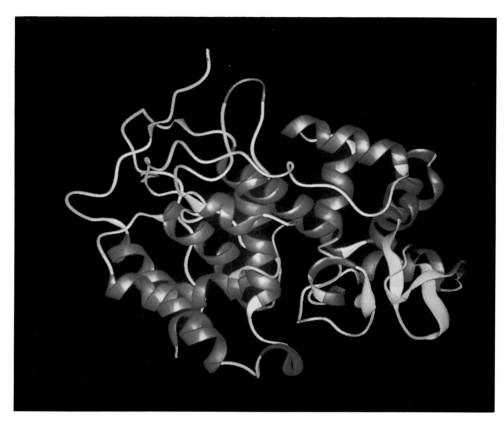

Left: The structure of an enzyme called CCP, displayed by computer. The ribbons represent chains of amino acids and actually involve hundreds of individual atoms. The model shows how these fold to create a unique tertiary structure.

in this way. For example, a beta-2 adrenergic receptor agonist (salbutamol) activates the appropriate receptor to cause a dilation of the bronchi to relieve asthma.

Researchers have found that the intermediate between the ligand-receptor complex and the adenylate cyclase is a group of proteins called *G proteins* (G because they bind guanosine diphosphate). When a chance mutation switches them permanently on, these may be involved in causing some cancers. The ras oncogene, for example, behaves as a permanent stimulus for growth and proliferation, leading to a tumor.

A development in the 1980s was the discovery of the phosphoinositide system by Berridge in the U.K. and Nishizuka in Japan. This second "second-messenger" system controls intracellular calcium levels. Two "second messengers", *diacylglycerol* and *inositol triphosphate*, are generated by the binding of an agonist. The latter causes the release of intracellular calcium stores, while diaglycerol activates protein *kinase C*, which requires the released calcium for its activity and in turn transfers phosphate groups to key proteins, switching them on to give a cellular response.

The folding problem

Proteins and enzymes are composed of 21 basic building blocks called amino acids common to all forms of life on Earth. The unique sequence of amino acids that makes up a protein or *polypeptide* chain contains all the information it needs to take up its correct three-dimensional shape. This shape, or *tertiary fold*, is crucial for biological activity. However, the precise shape of a protein cannot yet be predicted from its primary amino acid sequence alone. This is because the laws which govern the "folding" of polypeptide chains are not understood. Recently, biochemists have discovered that the folding process is often aided, and its efficiency increased, by helper proteins called *chaperonins*.

As X-ray CRYSTALLOGRAPHY or nuclear magnetic resonance (NMR) spectroscopy reveals more protein structures and amino acid sequences, biochemists have now come to realize that proteins and enzymes can be grouped into "superfamilies" with essentially the same tertiary fold. Perhaps some 30 per cent of enzyme superfamilies were known by the early 1990s.

It is also possible to model unknown protein structures using appropriate building blocks chosen from the wide range of known structures. The tools for this modeling process, increased availability of computing power coupled to high-resolution computer graphics, will eventually allow biochemists to design enzymes from scratch for specific purposes.

Bioengineering

Bioengineering, often confused with BIOTECHNOLOGY, can best be described as the application of engineering practice, principles, and thought to biological problems. But the vast majority of bioengineering, sometimes also called biomedical engineering or even, in rather science-fictional terms, bionics, is applied to medicine and medical research.

Some forms of bioengineering must rank among humankind's oldest skills. When primitive humans injured or lost a leg, they might have used a stick or a crutch, or extended the shortened limb with a piece of wood or bone. A substitute for any part of the body is called a prosthesis. In modern medicine external prostheses are available for limbs, hands, and feet while there are internal prostheses for most joints, short sections of larger blood vessels, and some bones, including those of the face and skull.

These may have been injured in accidents, removed because of disease, or had to be reshaped because they were the wrong shape at birth or failed to grow properly. Both internal and external prostheses have benefited enormously from the availability of modern materials which are light and strong, such as plastics, sometimes reinforced with carbon fiber, titanium, and recently, ceramics.

An example of the best engineering and materials practice is the modular artificial leg. While the socket is made from a precise plaster cast and measurements to fit the patient, the structure and mechanism is built up from a series of modules which are manufactured just like the components of a car engine. These are made in a range of sizes and different characteristics and then custom-assembled to suit the wearer.

Depending on the confidence and ability of the patient different knees can be fitted, some with a brake so that the lower leg can swing free until a load is applied, when it locks securely. With a mechanism like this giving security and confidence, many amputees are able to run, dance, play golf, and enjoy a full and active life. A plastic foam sheath, shaped like a natural leg, surrounds the bare components, while a skin-colored stocking gives the whole thing a very natural appearance.

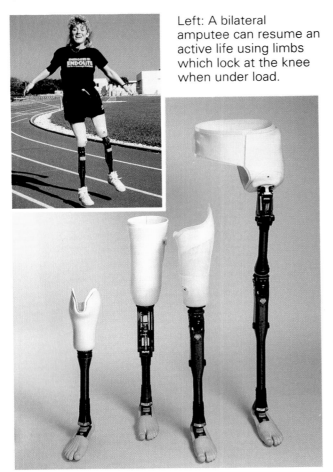

Left: A bilateral amputee can resume an active life using limbs which lock at the knee when under load.

Above: By using standard parts, a range of limbs can be provided to suit individual needs. The limbs are made of carbon fiber, and can be cut to length.

Above: The structure of the prosthesis can be effectively disguised using a plastic sheath. This man's left leg is completely artificial.

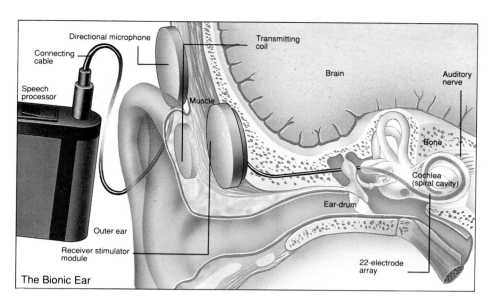

The Bionic Ear

Right: Many totally deaf people can now be given some hearing with a cochlear implant, which directly stimulates the nerve fibers of the inner ear in response to sound picked up by an external microphone. The sound quality is often restricted, however, and people who have never had hearing may be unable to decipher the unfamiliar sensation.

Currently, almost all artificial limbs are passive; that is, they are operated by the wearer's remaining muscle power rather than by any internal power source. There are two reasons for this. First, it is difficult to store enough energy in a limb to substitute, even for short periods, for the energy that would have been supplied by the muscles. Second, if the limb is to be moved unconsciously, rather than deliberately, it is difficult to obtain a sufficient number of control signals, perhaps from the electrical activity of muscles in the stump, to manage complex movements. An exception is the hand; there are powered versions of this, because the power requirements are modest and control signals can be obtained from the forearm.

An advance announced in 1992 is the "intelligent prosthesis", which uses microprocessor control to adjust the pneumatic damping of artificial legs to suit the wearer under a wide variety of conditions. Normally, the damping is set for a particular speed or gait, often resulting in a tiring limp at other speeds. But with active control, the limp can disappear and the wearer can become more agile.

Not all prostheses are mechanical. Some provide a substitute for a signal. The best known of these is the cardiac pacemaker. The heart's own natural pacemaker is a small piece of excitable tissue which, when modulated by nerve signals, controls the rate at which the heart beats. It is located between the atria and the ventricles. The electrical impulse it generates first causes the atria to contract, and is then conducted by a specialized short piece of nervous tissue to the ventricles, which perform the real work of pumping.

Implantable pacemakers are now the norm. The early models used comparatively primitive timing circuits, but pacemakers have now become smarter in a number of ways. Some emit pulses only when they recognize that the heart is not beating spontaneously at the correct rate, while others sense the weak pulse that the natural pacemaker produces in the atrium and use that to trigger the main pulse. Many can now be adjusted by telemetry from the outside to give optimum matching to the patient and they can also report their own performance to an external receiver, having kept a record of possibly a few million recent heartbeats.

Helping the blind to see

People who are blind because of damage to the retina of the eye or the optic nerve connecting it to the brain may still have a perfectly good visual cortex, the surface of the brain at the back of the head, where something like an electrical representation of the image appears. Work has been done at the Medical Research Council in England, to stimulate the cortex directly with electrical signals.

A silicone rubber mold carrying a 16 x 16 grid of electrodes is implanted underneath the patient's skull. The electrodes are in direct contact with the surface of the cortex and can each be addressed individually by a form of radio receiver.

Signals are transmitted by induction from a coil outside the head, as is the power needed to operate the receivers. The external transmitter can be connected to a television camera which also breaks up the pictures it sees into a 16 x 16 grid. The wearer experiences an arrangement of bright flashes which would, for example, allow single letters to be recognized.

There are technical difficulties in constructing such a prosthesis and preventing water from the tissue fluid from getting into the electrodes. These have in principle been solved and a small number of devices has been transplanted.

Biophysics

Biophysics is the application of physics techniques and physics "ways of thinking" to biological problems. One area where there has been a great deal of development recently is in "molecular biophysics" – what can we learn by the application of physical methods about the molecules of which we are built?

Some of the most significant biological molecules are very large, up to 1,000,000 times the size of a water molecule, and contain hundreds or thousands of atoms (water, H_2O, has only three atoms). Two of the major classes of these *macromolecules* are proteins (such as hemoglobin and collagen) and nucleic acids (DNA – deoxyribonucleic acid). It is the nucleic acids that store genetic information sufficient to determine our individual identities. Proteins are assembled using information carried by the nucleic acids to fulfill a variety of roles, such as enzymes speeding up biochemical reactions, or as structural molecules (in skin, bone, tendons, and hair), or as part of molecular machines such as muscle.

One of the great physics achievements this century has been the invention of methods to determine how the atoms in proteins or nucleic acids are organized. These structures, in turn, have revealed how the molecules function. For example, the structure of DNA, discovered in 1952, showed how genetic information in a cell could be duplicated and transferred to two identical daughter cells during cell division. It also showed how the information (the genetic message) needed to define a particular protein was actually stored. But how are these structures determined?

The level of detail that can be seen in an ordinary microscope depends on the nature of the "light" illuminating the specimen. With visible light (wavelength about $1/65,000$ in.), the largest objects that can be seen are about $1/150,000$ in. But molecular dimensions are about 100 times smaller than this. In order to study such small objects it is necessary to use very short wavelength radiation – such as X-rays, electrons, or neutrons.

X-rays have great penetrating power and appropriate "lenses" are very hard to make. But X-rays can interact with regular structures at the atomic or molecular level to give so-called diffraction patterns. In 1913, not long after X-rays were discovered (1895), it was found that they could be diffracted by crystals of, say, rocksalt (NaCl) to give beautiful diffraction patterns. In the 1930s, it was found that proteins could also produce crystals. One of the tremendous achievements of the middle part of the century was the invention of methods that could interpret diffraction patterns

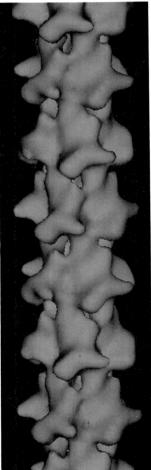

Above: The structure of the Foot and Mouth Disease virus, which was recently discovered using synchrotron radiation. The nucleic acid complex, seen in the center in red, is surrounded by protein complexes. By determining the structure of the virus, scientists are part way towards finding a cure for the potentially-disastrous disease.

Left: This image is an example of a structure that was computer-generated from an electron microscope image taken in 1991. It is a protein filament – a helical assembly of protein molecules – from the muscles which enable a giant water bug to fly. The diameter of the filament is about 20 nanometers.

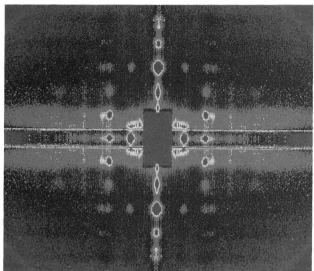

Above: A diffraction pattern, obtained through synchrotron X-ray, of a turbot's fin muscle. The regular pattern shows that the muscle is highly organized at a molecular level. In the image on the left, the muscle was at rest while the image on the right – in which the molecules have moved – was taken while the muscle was producing force. Each pattern was recorded in about five milliseconds.

from protein crystals to solve the structure of the protein molecule. Today, the structures of over 1000 macromolecules are known from X-ray CRYSTALLOGRAPHY and more are solved each week.

The best information from crystals of biological macromolecules is usually obtained if the X-ray beams are very intense. The most intense beams available for such studies are currently produced by large circular particle accelerators known as *synchrotrons*. There are not very many of these. In the U.S. they are located at major research centers such as those at Brookhaven, Stanford, and Cornell. The high intensity of the X-ray beams allows increasingly complex structures to be studied. For example, a recent success at the Daresbury Laboratory in the U.K. has been the determination of the structure of the Foot and Mouth Disease Virus (FMDV) – a complex of nucleic acid, surrounded by an outer spherical "shell" of protein. One of the benefits from knowing such a structure is that it is possible to use computer displays to help in the design of drug molecules that will interact with particular parts of the virus and so block its action. In the case of FMDV the potential benefits to agriculture are clearly enormous. The structures of a number of medically important viruses have also been solved.

As well as X-rays, it is possible to use electrons to study molecular structures. Their great advantage is that they carry a charge and so can be focused by electromagnetic "lenses" to produce images of the object. However, electron microscopes can only operate if they contain a vacuum; under such conditions, and with substantial electron irradiation, biological specimens are easily damaged. Much effort has gone into preserving molecular structures so that they can be "seen" in electron microscopes before they are destroyed. The images obtained are then often computer processed to provide more reliable information.

With modern electron microscope methods, it is possible to view the internal structure of protein molecules. Soon, for particular types of specimens, such as two-dimensional crystalline sheets of molecules, the resolution obtained will be comparable to that achieved with X-ray crystallography.

Observing molecule changes
One of the ambitions of many biologists is not just to determine molecular structures, but to be able to see changes in these molecules as they go through their normal activities. Muscle is a molecular machine in which protein molecules move on the timescale of milliseconds or less to produce muscular force. Can we follow these molecular movements to find out how muscle works?

In the 1990s, synchrotron X-ray sources are helping to find the answer to this problem. By using synchrotron radiation it is possible to record the pattern produced by muscle molecules in about five milliseconds. If the muscle is stimulated to produce force, it is found that the X-ray diffraction pattern changes as the molecules have moved. Biophysicists are now following changes in these patterns to determine the nature of the movements involved so that the origin of muscular force can be determined at the molecular level.

Biotechnology

In the two decades since scientists first learned how to cut, splice, and recombine genes, the use of living organisms to manufacture products has become a major industry. Genetically modified bacteria, yeasts, and other one-celled creatures are churning out new drugs, vaccines, and industrial chemicals with annual sales in billions of dollars, while modified plants and animals are increasing yields and reducing costs for farmers.

There is nothing new about using living organisms as factories. For centuries we have made beer and wine by fermentation and cheese by the action of natural enzymes on milk. For decades pharaceutical companies have used microorganisms to produce antibiotics. Usually, however, the term "biotechnology" is used to refer only to the manipulation of life at the molecular level.

Most of these technologies grow out of our understanding of how deoxyribonucleic acid (DNA) directs the manufacture of proteins. Each protein is a unique chain of amino acids, and a single gene – a segment of the long strand of DNA that makes up a chromosome – codes for that particular amino acid sequence. Biotechnology came into being when scientists learned how to insert a foreign gene into a living cell in such a way that it would be "expressed" – that is, so that the cell would make the protein for which it codes (see MOLECULAR BIOLOGY).

Perhaps the best-known product made in this way is human insulin. Others include human growth hormone, used to correct dwarfism, several forms of interferon, used to stimulate the immune system, and tissue plasminogen activator, used to dissolve blood clots to minimize the damage due to a heart attack. These are all substances which occur naturally in the human body; biotechnology has made it possible to produce them in large enough quantities to use as drugs.

Engineered bacteria

The technique most often used to make these products depends on the fact that the DNA in a bacterial cell is in the form of rings, called plasmids. Plasmids are removed from the cell, genes for the desired product are inserted in the ring, and the plasmids returned to cells. While producing all the other proteins normally needed in the course of bacterial life, each modified cell also manufactures the protein for which the inserted gene codes.

The most commonly used bacterium is *Escherichia coli (E. coli)*, found in the human intestine. (To avoid any possible side effect should the modified bacteria be released into the environment, most workers use a weakened strain called "K-12," which grows in artificial cultures but cannot survive in humans or animals.) Other simple organisms, including yeasts and fungi, as well as animal cells in culture, have been used.

Cells that take up and express the new gene are

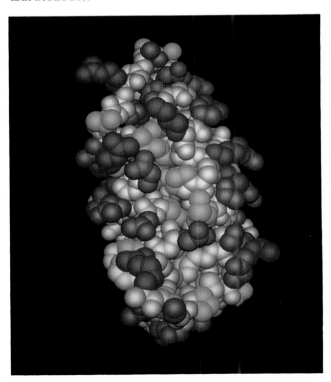

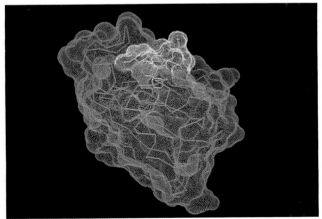

Left: Computer image of a biomanufactured protein, known as granulocyte-macrophage colony stimulating factor. Found naturally in the body, it stimulates the immune system and is used to treat blood disorders. The colors show electric charges. Above: An immunosuppressant drug, shown yellow, modeled by computer, showing how its shape precisely fits an immune-system protein, colored blue.

Right: The basic technique of genetic engineering takes DNA from plasmid rings in bacteria. These are then spliced using enzymes and a fragment of the desired DNA inserted. Those bacteria which express the gene are cultured on a large scale.

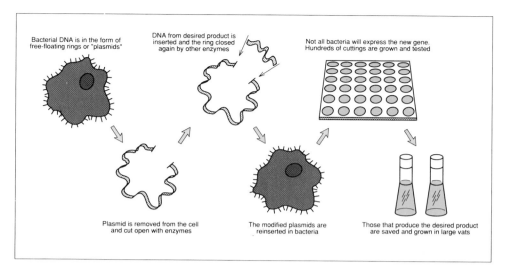

Bacterial DNA is in the form of free-floating rings or "plasmids"

DNA from desired product is inserted and the ring closed again by other enzymes

Not all bacteria will express the new gene. Hundreds of cuttings are grown and tested

Plasmid is removed from the cell and cut open with enzymes

The modified plasmids are reinserted in bacteria

Those that produce the desired product are saved and grown in large vats

separated, grown in large quantities and harvested, and the product is extracted from the soup of chemicals that results. Usually this is done by chromatography – the mixture is pulled through a porous material that separates substances by their molecular weight – or by forcing the mixture through membranes that select molecules by size. Because contaminants might remain, the resulting product must be rigorously tested for purity.

It is possible to insert genes in higher animals, but the process is much more difficult. Usually fertilized eggs are surgically removed, the new genes inserted through the cell wall, and the eggs reimplanted in the original or surrogate mothers. It may take hundreds of tries before the inserted gene is expressed. So far this sort of work has been confined to the laboratory; although many companies have obtained patents on genetically modified or "transgenic" animals, as of late 1992 none had been exploited commercially.

Safer vaccines

Genes have also been inserted into viruses to make vaccines. A virus has a protein coat which enables the virus to penetrate the outer membrane of a cell, plus DNA (or RNA) which codes for the proteins. Once inside a cell, the viral DNA uses the machinery of the cell to make copies of itself and of its protein coat, which reassemble into more viruses.

To defend against a virus or any other foreign invader, the immune system creates antibodies: complex molecules designed to fit the exact shape of a part of the virus protein coat – called an antigen – and attach to it. The purpose of a vaccine is to stimulate the immune system to make antibodies without forcing the body to experience the disease. One way to do this is by killing or "attenuating" the virus so it cannot reproduce. Unfortunately, if the virus is not completely deactivated the vaccine may cause the disease it was designed to prevent. Bioengineered vaccines are made by inserting the gene for an antigen into the DNA of an otherwise harmless virus, such as the *Vaccinia* virus used to immunize against smallpox. It is possible to add several genes to a single virus, producing a vaccine that protects against several illnesses at once.

Monoclonal antibodies

Biotechnology has provided a way to make antibodies to order. In the classic procedure a foreign

Left: Transgenic ewes, raised not for their wool or meat but for an enzyme which they produce in their milk and which is used to treat emphysema.

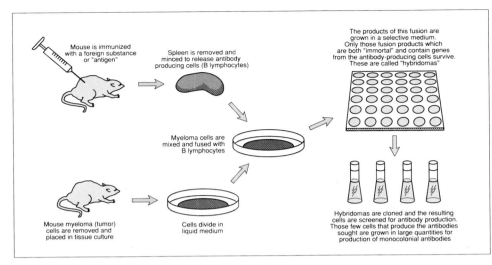

Mouse is immunized with a foreign substance or "antigen"

Spleen is removed and minced to release antibody producing cells (B lymphocytes)

The products of this fusion are grown in a selective medium. Only those fusion products which are both "immortal" and contain genes from the antibody-producing cells survive. These are called "hybridomas"

Myeloma cells are mixed and fused with B lymphocytes

Mouse myeloma (tumor) cells are removed and placed in tissue culture

Cells divide in liquid medium

Hybridomas are cloned and the resulting cells are screened for antibody production. Those few cells that produce the antibodies sought are grown in large quantities for production of monoclonal antibodies

Left: How monoclonal antibodies are produced. A mouse's immune system produces antibodies, while its cancer cells are "immortal". Combining the two gives everlasting identical antibodies.

antigen is injected into a mouse (or another animal), causing the mouse's immune system to create cells called B lymphocytes which produce antibodies to that antigen (see IMMUNOLOGY). A few days later B lymphocytes obtained from the mouse are fused with cancer cells, creating immortal cells called hybridomas. The hybridomas that produce the desired antibody are separated out and grown in a cell culture to make large quantities of just that antibody; since the antibodies are all alike they are called "monoclonal."

Monoclonal antibodies are widely used in clinical tests, such as those used to detect the presence of drugs or the AIDS virus. These tests use an antibody that will attach to the substance to be detected, and which is chemically linked to a radioactive or fluorescent tracer, or to an enzyme that will produce a color change in another chemical. A solution of these antibodies is mixed with a sample of blood, urine, or other body fluids or tissues, then treated to separate out only antibodies that have attached to a target. The presence of the tracer then signals a positive test. The most familiar example of this technology is the home pregnancy test.

Since it is now possible to synthesize DNA in any desired sequence, strands of DNA (or RNA) are in use as drugs and research tools. When the ladder-like double helix of DNA is split into two complementary chains, a short segment of DNA

Left: The larger mouse, the first transgenic animal, has a gene for rat growth hormone. It is 50 per cent bigger than its normal brother.

Left: A large-scale fermenter used for producing monoclonal antibodies on a commercial scale in batches of 525 gallons (2000 liters).

that is designed to be complementary to a gene will bind to that gene. Such "DNA probes" can be used to test for the presence of a particular gene in a DNA sample. Similarly, a strand of DNA or RNA can bind to a complementary gene in a living organism, inactivating it. A strand of nucleic acid used in this way is called an "anti-sense" drug. Such drugs may turn off the oncogene that causes a cancer cell to reproduce indefinitely.

Biotech in the chemical industry

The industry making the most use of biotechnology is of course the one which already deals with living creatures: agriculture. Plant breeders may now shorten the tedious process of crossing and recrossing plants, by simply inserting desirable genes for such traits as disease resistance into already successful crops. Bioengineered drugs and vaccines have enhanced the health of farm animals, and biomanufactured hormones promise to increase the yield of meat and milk. (See AGRICULTURAL SCIENCE.)

A future goal of biotechnology is to make proteins that do not already exist in nature. The biological activity of a protein is determined by its shape. The complex shape of an enzyme interlocks precisely with other molecules, causing them to react; the shape of a hormone connects with a receptor on the surface of a cell, and so on. By designing molecules with new shapes we might be able to cause new reactions or enhance existing ones.

• FACT FILE •

- The future of pharmaceutical manufacturing may lie not in vats of bacteria but in "biopharming" of higher plants and animals. Scientists have created transgenic (genetically modified) plants and animals that produce useful drugs.

- Pharmaceutical Proteins Ltd. in Edinburgh, Scotland has raised four transgenic ewes whose milk contains an enzyme called alpha-1 antitrypsin; persons lacking this enzyme run a particular risk of contracting emphysema. Five liters of milk from one ewe yielded enough of the enzyme to treat one patient for a year.

- Gene Pharming Europe B.V., a company in Leiden, The Netherlands, has reported creating cows whose milk contains lactoferrin, an antibacterial agent. Cows are considered the ideal animals to use as biofactories because they produce far more milk than sheep or goats, but the surgery to remove their eggs is much more difficult and expensive. The Dutch workers got around this by collecting eggs from a slaughterhouse and fertilizing them in a test tube.

- Workers at the Research Institute of Scripps Clinic in California have grown tobacco plants that produce antibodies. An antibody is made from two protein chains, so the researchers removed the two genes for these chains from animal cells and inserted one gene in each of two lines of plants. Later they crossed the two lines, and one-quarter of the offspring made complete antibodies. This method, they say, is vastly cheaper than making antibodies in mice, and raises the possibility of making plants with ready-made antibodies to plant diseases.

- Finally, a Japanese company has engineered silkworms to produce a vaccine for hepatitis B. The worms are squeezed to harvest the product.

Botany

Botany – the study of plants – is currently undergoing a revolution thanks to GENETIC ENGINEERING, and recent years have seen some of the most impressive advances. These new techniques are enabling botanists to design crop plants for bumper harvests.

Corn, for instance, can now chase off its worst pest, the European corn borer, by utilizing a gene which produces an insecticide within the plant that is toxic only to the bug and harmless to other creatures, including humans. The financial rewards could be considerable, since the insect causes crop losses worth $500 million a year in the United States alone.

For the first time, a gene has been implanted into wheat to make it resistant to herbicide. In this way, weeds in a field can be attacked and destroyed without harming the crop; and, much more importantly, genes for better protein quality and better disease resistance can be introduced into wheat in the future (see AGRONOMY).

Another advance provided by genetic engineering is the ability to turn the masculinity of plants on or off, which the breeder needs to do in order to raise pedigree crop strains. In crops like corn, for instance, the male anthers have physically to be ripped out of each plant, at a yearly cost in the U.S. of $200 million, to prevent them from breeding with other neighboring strains and so losing or diluting valuable characteristics. By emasculating the plants, breeders can cross them with a pollen of their choice, ensuring that they make a good hybrid.

Genetic engineering is promising other, even more extraordinary, achievements in botany. Farmers may in the future grow *plastics* as a crop. Genetic engineers in the U.S. have made thale cress – a plant with no commercial use so far – produce a natural plastic called PHB. The plastic has the great advantage of being biodegradable, and ICI (Britain's biggest chemicals company)

Below: Tobacco remains an important cash crop despite its narcotic properties, and is a standard testbed for research. Genetic engineering has helped produce bumper tobacco harvests, while food crops such as corn and wheat are now stronger and better able to resist pests and insecticides. One day, in the not too distant future, farmers may even be able to grow plastic as a crop.

already uses bacteria to make PHB commercially in fermenters, for use in products such as shampoo bottles, garden labels, and medical sutures.

Plants behaving like animals

During the 1980s, plant scientists started to realize that plants behave much more like animals than had been imagined. In particular, it appears that they have touch sensitivity and even a primitive ability to communicate with each other.

Dozens of plants, such as the Venus' Flytrap and Sensitive Plant (*Mimosa*), use a sense of touch to trigger their movements, but it is now becoming increasingly clear that botanical peculiarities such as these are far from unusual. In fact, all plants have a sense of touch, and this sense works uncannily like that in animals.

Simply stroking a plant's stem for a few seconds a day is enough to stunt its growth and widen its stem. In natural conditions this allows plants to stand up to the buffeting of the wind and prevents their stems from snapping. This is probably why Japanese farmers brush their sugar beet seedlings before transplanting them to the field, thus helping them to survive better. But scientists are now puzzled by other features of plant touch awareness. Stroking the plants also seems to be a sort of plant tonic: it increases their chlorophyll content and helps them endure drought or chilly periods. Horticulturalists are now looking to see how they can use these promising features in greenhouses and fields.

How does a plant's sense of touch actually work? In 1989 special touch sensors were discovered in plant cell membranes. When the cells are stretched the membrane sensors open up and let ions through, upsetting the voltage across the membrane. Exactly the same thing happens in animal cells, telling touch-sensitive nerves when to fire signals to alert the brain. It may seem farfetched that plants and animals behave in the same way, but in fact the Venus' Flytrap and *Mimosa* actually generate nerve-like electric signals when touched, to tell their motor cells to move. Even though plants have no nerves as such, their cells are joined together in a communication link of electric circuits.

It is not clear whether ordinary plants also use electric signals when they detect touch, but scientists are unravelling a string of chemical reactions triggered by the touch sensors which eventually lead to a change in the plant's growth and development. In 1990 an important discovery was made by chance at Stanford University. Janet Braam and Ronald Davis were looking at how plant genes work, when they noticed that touching or even simply spraying a plant with water triggered off a special set of genes. Chemical detective work

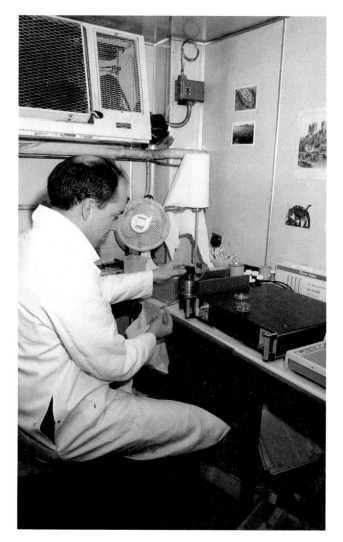

Above and right: Botanists are hard at work, genetically engineering new strains of plant in petri dishes. Thanks to the scientists' work in the past, corn is now able to repel its worst pest – the European corn borer – and wheat is able to resist the herbicides sprayed on fields to destroy weeds. Such discoveries are a boon for farmers.

revealed that these touch-sensitive genes make a protein involved in identifying and grabbing hold of calcium ions.

These calcium ions are a vital signal for redirecting plant growth, and in 1992 a group of researchers at Edinburgh University turned this chemistry into a practical tool. They genetically engineered a "glow" gene into potato plants to make them light up whenever they released calcium under stress. Simply touching the plant made its cells glow sky-blue, and the researchers hope that farmers will eventually use light meters to gauge plant health.

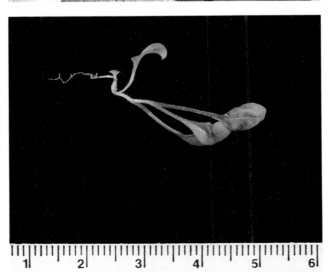

Plant talk

Several remarkable pieces of research have revealed a chemical language between plants. Interest in this began when oak trees being attacked by caterpillars were found to respond by making bitter-tasting tannins, which insects find distasteful. Unexpectedly, nearby unmolested trees started producing the tannins, as if under caterpillar attack, as well. It appeared that somehow the infested trees had been able to warn their neighbors.

Exactly how tree can talk to tree remained a mystery until, in 1990, a perfumed signal was discovered in sagebrush, a plant familiar from so many cowboy movies. When a sagebrush is attacked by insects it not only starts making special insect-fighting proteins, but also gives off a hormone perfume rather like the scent of jasmine, telling neighboring plants to switch on their insect-repelling proteins.

Airborne signals are also used by plants to recruit helpful insects. In 1990, it was found that a scent released by corn plants under attack from caterpillars appeared to act like an SOS signal and attracted passing wasps. These were not ordinary wasps, however, but parasitic ones which laid their eggs on the caterpillars, eventually killing them. The plant was attracting the natural enemies of its own enemy, the caterpillar, using a chemical language.

Meanwhile, below ground level, desert plants have been discovered telling one another to keep their distance. When roots from different plant species grow near each other they often avoid tangling with one another by giving off warning signals. They pass chemical messages into the soil, which in effect reveal if the plant is the same species or a competitor.

Aspirin

In addition to airborne hormone signals, many other hormones are being discovered in plants. Probably the most unusual is aspirin, although it has been known for many decades that plants make aspirin – in fact the very name aspirin comes from *Spiraea*, or meadowsweet. But until recently no one could figure out what function this drug fulfilled in plants.

The answer came – like so many major scientific discoveries – from a completely unexpected source. The Voodoo Lily is a tropical plant with an extraordinary bloom. On the outside it looks like a purple poker wrapped up in a green sheath, nipped at the bottom into a small chamber. When the bloom becomes fertile the poker suddenly heats up, exuding a pungent foul-smelling odor. This "perfume" attracts flies, which flock to the poker and crawl down the sheath to the inside of

Right and middle: Studies of aspirin-producing plants such as the Voodoo Lily *(Sauromatum venosum)* and touch-sensitive plants like the Venus' Flytrap *(Dionaea muscipula)* are helping scientists to create stronger, more hardy plants.
Bottom: Incredibly, the *Chlamydomonas* alga contains a chemical light sensor which is almost identical to that found in the eyes of mammals.

the chamber where the real flowers are hidden, and pollinate them.

The signals that trigger the poker to heat up were unknown until the chemistry of the bloom was unravelled in 1987. Of all the chemicals in the plant, only one candidate fitted the bill – salicylic acid, the chemical cousin of aspirin. Its levels surged just before the poker heated up.

This discovery led scientists to investigate how salicylic acid affected ordinary plants. They found that plants attacked by diseases make salicylic acid to fight the infection. It is also thought the chemical allows them to withstand bouts of cold weather. Companies are now looking at ways of either applying the chemical to crops, or breeding plants with high levels of their own salicylic acid.

Plant hormones

Although plant growth hormones have been studied for some time, botanists may be on the threshhold of an exciting new wave of plant hormone research. Apart from salicylic acid, dozens of other hormones are being discovered, with prospects for future use in agriculture to promote growth and protect plants. Fascinatingly, most of them are closely related to animal hormones.

Prostaglandins, found in bean seedlings, are more commonly found in animals, where they trigger pain in wounds and areas of inflammation. Their purpose in plants remains unclear, however. The nerve-transmitting hormones serotonin, norepinephrine, and acetylcholine are found in vegetation from nuts to nettles, but it is not clear what their precise functions are. Acetylcholine seems to be involved in plant "clocks", telling the time of day and year by recording the hours of daylight each day. Animals seem to use acetylcholine for the same purpose, as well as for passing messages between nerve fibers.

Steroids are best known for their effects on humans, but estrogens and testosterones are found to help flowering in a wide variety of plants and even mating in fungi. Indeed, one of the most common plant hormones, gibberellic acid, is a close cousin of the animal sex hormones. So, too, are the other plant hormones: indoleacetic acid is related to a nerve impulse transmitter in animals, cytokinins are found in insects, and abscisic acid has been found in pig brains.

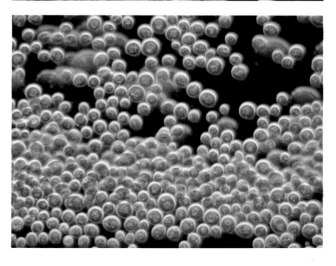

Building construction

The 1980s was the decade when skyscraper office blocks and hotels were hurriedly built in the rush to cash in on the worldwide economic boom. The lean years of the 1990s, in contrast, appear to be preoccupied with thrifty, environmentally friendly, and healthy buildings, amounting to a Green Revolution in architecture.

Green architecture primarily means buildings that use little or no commercially supplied energy in the form of fossil fuels or electricity. Burning the fossil fuels of petroleum, gas, and coal depletes the Earth's deposits of these non-renewable resources, so that they become scarcer and more expensive. Buildings are the greediest culprits, responsible for 50 per cent of the world's fossil fuel consumption through their internal services such as heating, lighting, hot water supply, air conditioning, and elevators. Using electricity only shifts the problem to central power stations, which also burn fossil fuels or, alternatively, nuclear fission, which presents its own environmental risks.

In temperate climates, half the energy used up in buildings goes into heating the interiors. Therefore, the most obvious way of saving energy in buildings is to stop heat escaping through exter-

Right: Roof panels are an increasingly common sight. These provide water heating, and can reduce the need for conventional heating even on a cold, cloudy day.

Above: This solar home in Corrales, New Mexico, makes use of abundant sunlight to heat water in drums, which is then circulated around the house using power generated by the windmill. The reflective walls keep the home cool during the day, while the small windows prevent sunlight from heating the interior by day and heat escaping through the glass at night.
Right: This energy-efficient "Round House" design incorporates an earth bank to help insulate the living area. Warm air can be extracted from the kitchen and bathroom and used elsewhere.

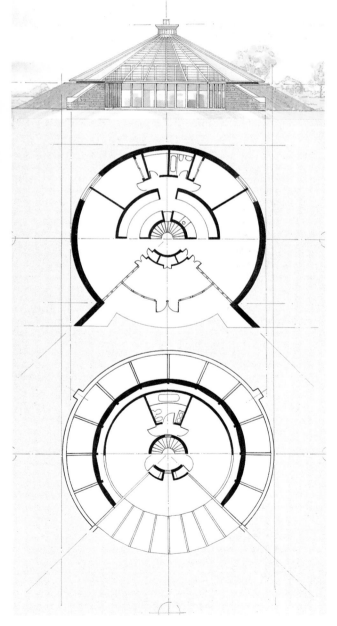

Right: An "intelligent building" in which all communication and supply systems are linked. 1: Telecommunications inputs; 2: Computers; 3: Communications outlets; 4: heat pump–chiller; 5: Building management controllers; 6: Environmental controllers; 7: Power supplies; 8: Heating, ventilation and air conditioning.

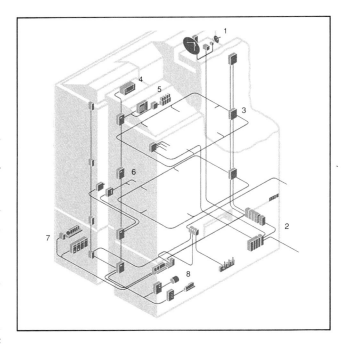

nal walls, roofs, windows, and doors by increasing thermal insulation and by blocking drafts.

Next, the services within a building are being made more efficient so that they use less energy to produce the same results. On a more sophisticated level, the entire energy consumption of a building can be controlled, minute by minute, night and day, by a centralized electronic building management system which can sense when a room has been vacated and then turn off heating and lights.

An "intelligent building" such as this is arguably the most revolutionary building type of the 1990s. Its innovations take the form of advances in MICROELECTRONICS information technologies, which are incorporated inconspicuously into the fabric and workings of the building. In an intelligent building, heating, lighting, air conditioning, power supply, and security systems are all monitored and automatically controlled by a central computer or building management system.

The true intelligent building is one that monitors and manages the workings of the building, as well as the electronic equipment of those using it, and even the spaces they occupy at different times. By integrating different technologies and responding to complex change, intelligent buildings are causing a revolution in the way organizations and people use them.

A more radical approach is to abandon commercially supplied energy sources in favor of harnessing the Earth's free and renewable sources of energy – sunshine and wind. Hot water and electricity can be actively generated by banks of solar collectors and solar cells, respectively, which can be conveniently located on roofs, as can wind-powered electric turbines.

Another approach is to mold the whole shape of a building to make the best use of sun and wind. Although more adventurous, this is a passive approach, as it relies on the natural physical properties of sun and wind to heat or cool spaces directly, rather than on gadgets to generate and distribute hot water or electricity. To heat a building passively, sunlight is admitted through windows and its heat is soaked up by floors and walls of massive concrete or masonry. Cooling can also be solar powered, where openings are strategically located to induce natural drafts right through a building. Surprisingly, even in cold climates very little heating is needed as long as the building makes the best use of what solar power is available.

Pollution can also pose health risks to people inside buildings. Harmful building materials such as asbestos, lead-based paints, and some chemical timber preservatives have been banned. Attention is now turning to internal air pollution, which, ironically, is often increased by crude attempts to save energy by making a building airtight.

A case in point is radon, which is a dangerously radioactive yet entirely natural gas that is emitted by certain geological rocks, such as granite. The only effective way to prevent radon seeping up into buildings erected in sensitive locations is to leave a void between the ground surface and the lowest floor and ventilate it thoroughly.

Sick Building Syndrome

The most mysterious illness induced by buildings has only recently been identified: Sick Building Syndrome. Its symptoms are headaches, drowsiness, and throat irritations.

Sick Building Syndrome is not a specific infection, but can be brought on by a collection of complaints, each one relatively innocuous in itself, such as poor ventilation, lack of views, and overheating, all of which are not uncommon in large buildings. It is often triggered by the building of new internal partitions, which subsequently give off fumes from the paint and other volatile substances used in the manufacture of the materials.

Large companies are finding out that economizing too much on energy consumption and space usage within their buildings can end up being very expensive, if it leads to their staff being afflicted with Sick Building Syndrome.

Cardiology

Advances in cardiology and respiratory medicine have improved the quality and length of life of people with heart disease. These advances are of three main kinds: new drugs, new techniques, and new technology.

Heart attacks and strokes occur when a blood clot blocks a crucial blood vessel, which is narrowed by deposits, called plaques, of a cholesterol-like material. The tissues of the heart or brain are starved of blood and hence the oxygen it carries. The "clotbusters" are new drugs that dissolve blood clots. They must be given intravenously as rapidly as possible, within 12 hours of the stroke or heart attack. There are two main kinds of clotbuster, both developed in the mid 1980s. Streptokinase activates plasminogen to form thrombin, which degrades the fibrin that holds the clot together. Tissue plasminogen activator has a similar method of action but is less effective.

New work on aspirin shows that regular small doses reduce the risk of heart attack and stroke. No one is yet clear how small a dose is needed, but it is probably the equivalent of one ordinary tablet of junior aspirin a day.

New drugs called ACE inhibitors (angiotensin converting enzyme inhibitors) prevent the un-

wanted conversion by enzymes of angiotensin I to angiotensin II, which constricts blood vessels. Introduced in the mid-1980s, they have a dual effect: they are yet another treatment for high blood pressure and have greatly improved the treatment of congestive heart failure.

Heart surgery has been continually refined over the last decade and transplantation has become almost a routine operation. This is largely due to techniques in IMMUNOLOGY. Cyclosporin, an immunosuppressive drug, reduces the body's capacity to reject the transplanted heart.

A new experimental technique may supersede

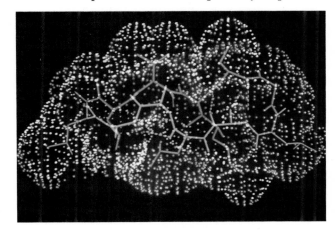

Above right: A computer graphic rendering of the cyclosporin molecule. Cyclosporins are used to reduce the risk of rejection of transplanted tissue.
Right: An infant boy is given oral cyclosporin-A through a syringe after a heart transplant.

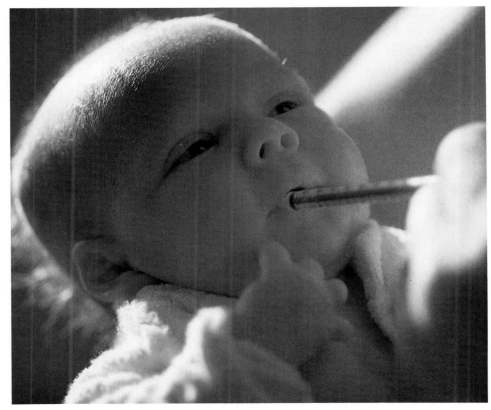

Right: During cardiac surgery, the patient's blood is diverted through a heart-lung machine which temporarily takes over the pumping and oxygenating of the blood.

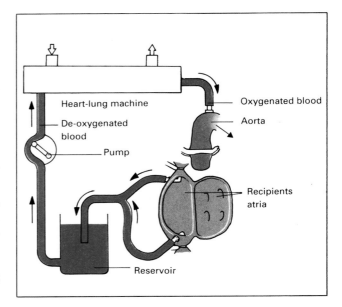

heart by-pass surgery. At present, if the coronary arteries that supply the heart itself get blocked, they are replaced with vessels taken from elsewhere in the patient, such as in the leg. This requires massive surgery, as the ribcage must be split down the middle and winched open to gain access to the heart. In 1992, surgeons were experimenting with drilling holes in the heart muscle, using a laser, so that blood that is pumping through the heart is also suffusing it and supplying it with oxygen. This can be done through a tiny incision in the chest; the ribcage does not need to be opened.

The incidence of heart disease reached a peak around 1970 and is now declining. No one knows why. Recent British research has shown that adults with the healthiest hearts are those who were well-fed in the uterus and in the first year of life. Records show that good feeding of pregnant women and babies will do far more to reduce heart disease in later life than any other dietary change.

Most people who die of heart attacks or suffocation do so in four minutes – too soon for a doctor or ambulance to arrive. Since the early 1980s there have been public education campaigns in many parts of the western world to train people in resuscitation. The training takes only two hours and the techniques can be learned by anyone aged 10 or over. The world's best-trained city is Seattle, where over half the patients who suffer heart attacks survive enough to return to paid work because a passer-by has saved their lives.

Respiratory diseases have also changed in incidence and treatment. Mild asthma is more common, especially in childhood, and scientists think this may be because more homes have central heating, so that the windows are closed, and the resulting warmth and humidity increase the numbers of house-dust mites. Lung cancer is becoming rarer in men and more common in women because of changing habits of smoking.

New treatments for asthma give virtually instant relief with fewer adverse side-effects. Drugs such as salbutamol, which were formerly taken only by mouth, are now inhaled. Because they arrive directly at the lung without going through the gut and circulatory system, relatively tiny doses are needed and are rapidly effective. Most people with chronic asthma now also inhale steroids, which reduce the frequency and severity of attacks. Very severe asthma, which was formerly difficult to treat, has been shown to respond extremely well to cyclosporin.

• FACT FILE •

- Imagine a heart whose arteries are clogged with plaque, which suddenly ruptures. A swarm of platelets – tiny blood cells concerned with clotting – moves to the scene, trying to repair the injured artery's walls. This is what happens in unstable angina, and it is a warning of impending heart attacks.

- New findings show that people hospitalized with unstable angina face a higher risk of heart attack if their blood contains cardiac troponin C, a protein that helps the heart contract. Normally present only in the heart, this is released if heart cells are damaged. In 1992, Christian Hamm of Hamburg University Hospital, Germany found it was present in 39 per cent of patients who had chest pain while resting – the most serious form of unstable angina. Of these 39 per cent, 10 later had a heart attack or died in hospital.

- However, of the patients whose pain subsided during hospital rest, none later went on to have heart attacks or die in hospital. Commenting, Dr. James H. Chesebro of the Mayo Clinic said that testing for troponin C can detect small amounts that sound a warning, so that patients can be given greater protection from blood clots.

Cell biology

Every living thing is composed of cells, from single-celled organisms such as bacteria to complex multi-cellular organisms – including humans. All cells share some common features, such as an outer membrane that controls what can enter or leave, but there are also vast differences. Multicellular organisms are made up of many different kinds of cells working together. In order to achieve this the cells must be able to communicate. Recent research has greatly expanded our understanding of how this communication works.

Cells communicate by releasing chemical messengers, including hormones which may travel through the bloodstream to distant targets, and *neurotransmitters* which nerve cells use to signal adjacent cells. When these messenger molecules reach a target cell, they usually attach to a *receptor*, a protein that is part of the cell membrane.

This receptor extends through the membrane. The part exposed on the outside has a structure which exactly fits the shape of one particular messenger molecule; inside the cell it has a structure which is able to interact with chemicals called *effectors*. Some receptors cross the membrane only once and are described as *single transmembrane domain receptors*. Others have as many as seven transmembrane domains.

When a messenger molecule binds to the outer part of the receptor it can change the shape of the entire receptor, including the inner structure. The inner structure then reacts with an effector, which often is an enzyme that converts another molecule into a *second messenger*, which diffuses through the interior of the cell triggering further reactions. Other receptors transmit their message across the membrane by transporting the messenger molecule itself through the membrane and releasing it inside.

Still other receptors form a channel that can be opened and closed when a messenger binds to the receptor, allowing other molecules to flow into the cell. These are called *ion channels*, which are found in nearly all cells. Ion channels are responsible for generating the electrical currents which carry signals along nerve fibers. These channels open in response to a neurotransmitter molecule released by an adjacent neuron or nerve cell, allowing sodium and potassium to pass through the channel, generating an electrical signal. In sensory organs ion channels translate physical or chemical stimuli into electrical signals for the nervous system.

The role of G proteins in signaling
Many receptors rely on molecules called *G proteins* to carry signals from the receptor to the rest of the cell. G proteins (short for "guanine nucleotide-binding") act as on-off switches. They are made up

Below: How the arrival of a hormone triggers a cell to release glucose. The hormone – here epinephrine – binds to its receptor. This causes the G protein to activate an effector which in turn converts the energy molecule STP into cyclic AMP. A cascade of reactions follow, which stimulate phosphorylase to convert glycogen into glucose.

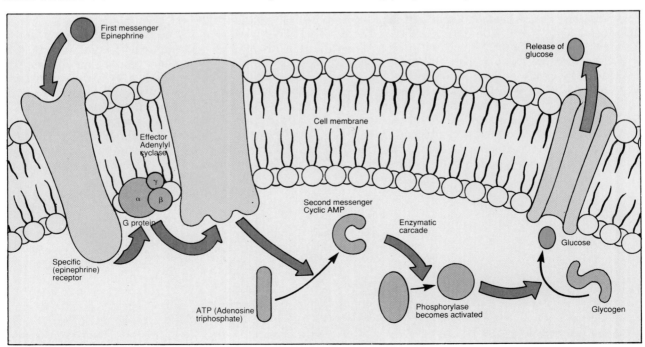

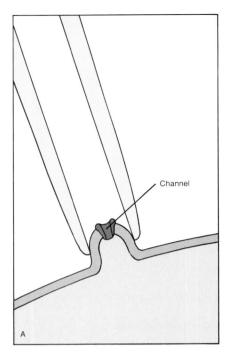

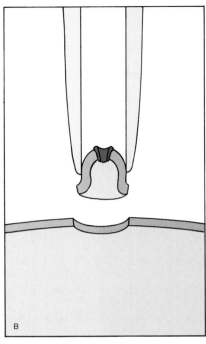

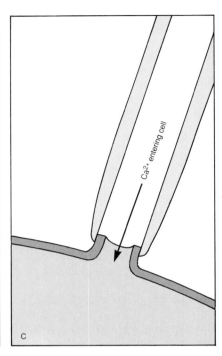

of three protein subunits termed α, β and γ. In the unstimulated state the α-subunit has GDP (guanosine diphosphate) bound to it, and the switch is off. When a chemical messenger binds to a receptor, changing its shape, this causes the α-subunit to exchange GDP for GTP (guanosine triphosphate) which is present in the cell. The α-subunit, with bound GTP, dissociates from the βγ subunit, diffuses along the membrane, and activates its effector molecule: the switch is on. After a few seconds the α-subunit converts the bound GTP to GDP by removing one of its three phosphate groups, thereby inactivating itself. The α-subunit reassociates with the βγ subunits and the switch is off again.

Independent work by Lubert Stryer at Stanford and Mark Bitensky at Yale revealed that the visual receptor system, which gives us our sight, works in a similar way. When rhodopsin, the light receptor in the retina cells of the eye, is struck by light, it activates transducin (the G protein in retinal cells), which activates an enzyme causing ion channels in the membrane to close, sending an

Above: Patch clamping involves a microscopic pipette. This enables researchers to isolate individual ion channels (A), which can then be detached from the cell membrane (B). The pipette can also be used to insert different constituents, such as calcium, into the cell interior (C).

electrical signal along the optic nerve to the brain. The advantage of this is that G proteins also amplify signals: one light receptor molecule can activate more than 500 G protein molecules almost simultaneously.

Studies of signaling systems that rely on G proteins have already improved our knowledge of several diseases. The bacteria responsible for cholera and whooping cough both secrete a toxin that cause G protein pathways to be over-activated. Defects in some G proteins can lead to uncontrolled proliferation of cells, as in cancer. Confirming this, Henry Bourne and his colleagues at the University of California at San Francisco have found mutated G proteins in the cells of pitu-

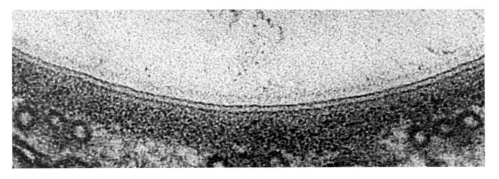

Left: An electron micrograph of a cell membrane, enlarged 500,000 times. The membrane consists of a sandwich of lipid, protein and lipid, through which ion channels pass, though these do not show up in an electron micrograph.

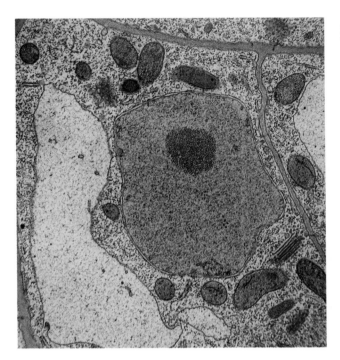

Above: False-color electron micrograph of a plant cell. The nucleus is shown pink, with the cytoplasm yellow. The circular blue features are mitochondria, while the elongated green parts are proplastids. These, the thick cell wall and the pale holes (vacuoles) distinguish this as a plant cell.

itary tumors. Other mutations in receptors and G proteins have been reported in patients with diabetes and pseudo-hypoparathyroidism. As knowledge of the G protein family expands it should be possible to design drugs to interact selectively with mutated G proteins, correcting defective cells while leaving healthy cells untouched.

Patch clamp technique

The study of ion channels is made much easier by the development of a technique called patch clamping. Erwin Neher and Bert Sakmann of the Max Planck Institute in Germany were awarded the 1991 Nobel Prize for Physiology or Medicine for describing the function of single ion channels using patch clamping.

The technique is simple: the open end of a thin glass tube called a pipette, 1/25,000 the diameter of a human hair, is tightly sealed against a cell membrane, isolating a small patch of the membrane and the ion channels it contains. An experimenter can then apply stimuli from within the pipette and measure the behavior of the trapped channel or channels. Alternatively, the membrane patch may be detached from the cell, exposing the interior face of the channel. And finally, if the membrane patch can be ruptured without break-

ing the seal between the pipette and the membrane, the cell's interior becomes accessible for manipulation via the pipette.

Patch pipettes can also be used to study signaling mechanisms at a cellular level, a procedure called voltage clamp analysis. Even human red blood cells and platelets, cells only a few microns in diameter, have been voltage clamped with patch pipettes. This means that most cell types of clinical interest can be studied; now many disorders, such as cystic fibrosis, have been traced back to defects in channel function.

Biological roles of nitric oxide

Most of the body's functions are regulated by large and complex proteins and compounds. However, nitric oxide, a simple gas that is noxious, has been discovered to be an extremely important messenger molecule.

Regulation of blood pressure is a balance between dilation (opening) and constriction (tightening) of blood vessels. Blood vessels are dilated by neurotransmitters such as *acetylcholine* that cause the muscle layer of the vessels to relax. Other neurotransmitters, such as *norepinephrine*, contract the muscle and constrict blood vessels. Because norepinephrine receptors are present on muscle cells, most scientists assumed the cells would also bear receptors for acetylcholine. It turned out that acetylcholine acts not on muscle cells but on receptors located on the adjacent endothelial cells that line the blood vessel, releasing a small molecule that diffuses to the muscle layer to relax it. This small molecule was termed endothelium-derived relaxing factor or EDRF until, in 1987, Salvador Moncada, a scientist at Wellcome Research Labs in England, demonstrated that EDRF is identical to nitric oxide. Nitric oxide is now believed to be the principal regulator of blood pressure.

Nitric oxide appears to play another major role in the brain. Glutamate, a neurotransmitter which is active at more sites in the brain than any other, is now believed to excite cells by a process that uses nitric oxide.

The next dramatic observation was that nitric oxide synthase, an enzyme that generates nitric oxide from the amino acid *arginine*, is found mainly in neurons – specifically in *diaphorase* neurons, which make up about two per cent of the cerebral cortex. The reason this distribution is so interesting is that these neurons alone resist the degeneration associated with several diseases. In Huntington's disease up to 95 per cent of neurons in an area called the caudate nucleus degenerate, but virtually no diaphorase neurons are lost. In vascular strokes and in some brain regions involved in Alzheimer's disease, diaphorase neurons are similarly resistant. Knowing how diaphorase neurons resist degeneration might provide treatments for these diseases.

It is believed that the neurons which make nitric oxide release it and due to its toxicity, it is capable of killing adjacent neurons. However, the cells producing the nitric oxide may have intrinsic defense mechanisms protecting against damage. Very recently Bernard Scatton and his colleagues at Synthelabo in Paris injected small doses of a nitric oxide synthase inhibitor into mice immediately after initiating a stroke, and stroke damage was reduced by 73 per cent.

Another unrelated activity of nitric oxide is as one of the major weapons of the white blood cells of the immune system, which use its toxic nature to kill bacteria, fungi, and tumor cells. It is also capable of inhibiting blood clotting by preventing the clumping of platelets.

For an apparently noxious compound, nitric oxide is involved in an impressive array of activities. There is now some work implicating carbon monoxide, familiar to us as a toxic gas in car exhaust, as having some signaling role in a number of brain regions. Could this be the second member of a new group of novel neurotransmitters, and if so, what other unexpected properties will it have?

Right: Fluorescent dyes can be used to stain specific cells in living animals. This is a photomicrograph of neuromuscular synapses – connections – in a living mouse. The horizontal bands are the muscle fibers. The mitochondria within the motor nerve terminals appear bright green.

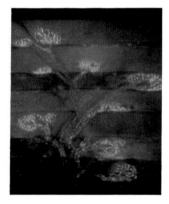

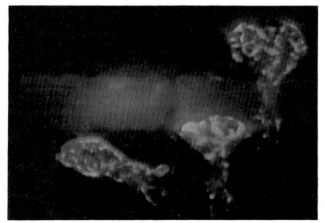

• FACT FILE •

- While studying a mouse tumor called a *teratoma*, Howard Green and James G. Rheinwald at Harvard Medical School found a way to grow mouse cells called *keratinocytes* in culture. This broad category includes cells of the epidermis, the outer layer of the skin. The same method made it possible to grow human keratinocytes, a feat which was previously impossible. This provides a method to replace human skin which has been destroyed by burns.

- Keratinocytes used to grow new skin must be donated by the patient to be treated. A piece of skin about 1½ in. (3 cm) square can be expanded within three to four weeks into nearly enough to cover the body surface of an adult.

- The surface to be grafted is usually highly contaminated with microorganisms which can damage skin grafts grown in culture, so the burn area is first covered with skin grafts from cadavers. These allow the patient's defense mechanisms to destroy the microorganisms. The foreign grafts are eventually destroyed by the patient's immune system, and are replaced by the patient's cultured skin.

- As yet, only a few cell types can be grown in culture. When we know more about the biology of each cell type and how to apply this knowledge to its cultivation, it might be possible to treat diabetes with cultured pancreatic islet cells, use cultured liver cells to repair liver failure, treat muscle disease with cultured myoblasts, or replace damaged or degenerated brain tissues. Also in the future is the prospect of using cultured cells to treat patients with genetic defects. Cells from the patient grown in culture could be genetically engineered to synthesize a product lacking in the body, then grafted back into the patient.

Left: Fluorescence photomicrograph of young living adult mouse fiber, stained to show the motor nerve terminals in green, and also stained with rhodamine which binds to acetylcholine receptors, coloring them red. This shows the link between motor nerve terminals and acetylcholine receptors.

Chaos theory

The theory of chaos studies ways in which order can be found among seemingly random events, be they natural or mathematical. Although it has recently become important in several scientific fields, as a branch of mathematics it was opened up by the distinguished French mathematician Henri Poincaré in 1893.

Poincaré showed that the motion of a satellite attracted to the Earth and the Moon could be so complicated that it could not even be drawn. Such motion deserves to be called chaotic, even though it is completely predictable as long as the starting conditions are known exactly.

Progress in chaos theory generally had to wait for the advent of high-speed computers. These revealed chaotic behavior in many areas that had seemed otherwise merely difficult to understand, such as weather prediction. Chaos theory then aims to find order underneath the chaos. For example, Edward Lorenz's equations for modeling the weather can be made to draw a curve in space describing how the weather parameters vary one with another – like a graph but with more than two variable quantities. The result is a striking butterfly-shaped figure, called Lorenz's strange attractor. It shows that only slight alterations in the starting conditions can considerably alter the subsequent behavior. This is like saying that a butterfly flapping its wings in Brazil could set off a tornado in Texas, making accurate prediction nearly impossible.

The pattern does, however, reveal that the evolution of the weather is constrained to a limited range of possibilities. The problem is then how to describe them. One way would be to get a measure of how thick the set of possibilities is. Is it a curve (one dimension), a surface (two dimensions), a solid tube (three dimensions), or something in between? Sets with a fractional dimension had been discovered at the start of century and are called fractals. They were brought back to life in the 1970s by Mandelbrot at IBM, and have subsequently been much studied by many eminent mathematicians.

A simple fractal is easy to draw as the limit of a series of successive approximations. Start with a triangle whose angles are 30°, 30°, and 120°; the first "curve" is composed of the two shorter sides. Replace this triangle with two smaller ones built from it but having the same angles. The new path is composed of the four equal shorter sides. At each stage, replace the triangles by similar smaller ones in the same way; the curve is formed from all the equal shorter sides. These curves steadily approximate to the one we want, which is a contin-uous curve that nowhere has a tangent – it is truly crinkly. Vary the triangle and other limiting curves are obtained. Many beautiful computer-generated images have been produced by taking a comparatively simple rule and continuing the process in this way.

Such crinkly sets arise in many areas of mathematics, typically when a number or set of numbers is repeatedly subjected to the same process. For example, when finding approximate solutions to equations, the output of a formula will be used as the new input until a sufficient degree of accuracy is obtained. Even the simplest examples of *iteration* (as such a repetitive process is called) are surprisingly delicate. One famous example is an iterative process in which a pair of numbers (thought of as a point in the plane) generates another pair. Points within the main region settle down, points outside move off to infinity, and points on the crinkly boundary move in a variety of ways around the boundary. Such sets are called Julia sets, after

Left: A Julia set, plotted on a computer graphics program by repeatedly carrying out a basic mathematical operation. Small parts of it have a similarity to the longer structures within it. Below: A Mandelbrot set reveals chaotic behavior, with certain points departing from the main structure.

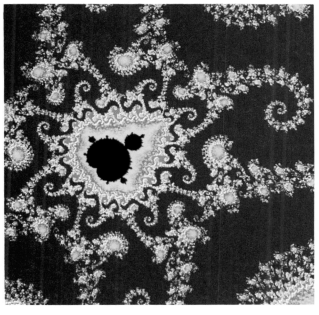

Gaston Julia, who was one of the first people to study them.

Some Julia sets come in one piece, others are scattered like dust. The Mandelbrot set describes which are which. Questions about the boundaries of Julia sets and the Mandelbrot set are presently much studied. Are they fractals? Sometimes they are, sometimes not. Julia sets are interestingly self-similar: if you take a small piece of one and enlarge it, it often looks like the original, which makes them very crinkly objects indeed. Remarkably, it was shown in 1991 that the boundary of the Mandelbrot set is not a curve but has two dimensions.

Right: The Lorenzian waterwheel is a simple demonstration of a chaotic system. 1. Water fills a bucket and starts the wheel turning. 2. At a certain flow, the wheel flows steadily. 3. If the water flow increases, the wheel turns faster, the buckets cannot empty in time, and the wheel reverses its motion. This sequence will repeat in random and chaotic fashion.

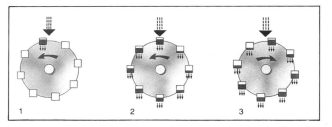

Left: The Lorenz attractor is generated by plotting several variable quantities together. The line, after remaining close to one point, suddenly departs for a different area of the plot, then just as suddenly returns again.
Below left: How to construct a simple fractal. The first stage is a triangle. Make two more triangles from two of the original slides, and continue. The boundary takes on an increasing complexity.

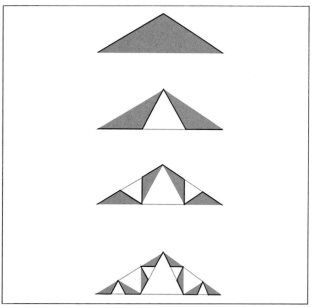

• FACT FILE •

- Aurorae – the northern lights – are notoriously hard to predict. A strong aurora can cause major communications breakdowns, as happened on March 13, 1989 when a huge aurora was seen over much of North America and Europe.

- A team of researchers announced in 1992 that one of the reasons for the sudden start of an aurora is that the motion of charged particles in the Earth's magnetic field can become chaotic extremely rapidly – in a matter of minutes.

- Sandra Chapman and Nick Watkins, of Sussex University in the UK, studied what happens to a particle trapped in the Earth's magnetic field when the field varies. They discovered that under certain circumstances it can rapidly alter its motion from a regular, predictable state to one where its path becomes quite unpredictable. Further information about the conditions in the rarefied upper atmosphere is needed to further investigate the theory. Satellites due for launch in 1995 may help resolve the problem.

Chemical technology

The bulk manufacturing side of chemistry is known as chemical technology, and the people who turn research work into a commercial supply are chemical engineers. They must have not only a wide knowledge of chemistry, but also physics, mechanics, and construction materials. A wide range of common products is the result of chemical processes, including rubber, paint, plastics, soap, organic chemicals, synthetic fibers, and agrochemical and pharmaceutical products. Whatever the result, chemical processes usually include some basic steps, and developments have taken place in each of these over the past few years.

Mixing

The first critical step in chemical manufacture is mixing. Chemicals are mixed together so that they undergo a chemical reaction to form the required product. In the simplest case this is a single reaction but in many others a whole sequence of reactions may be needed to arrive at the final product. Usually the chemicals, known as reactants, are pumped into a reactor vessel and stirred by a motor-driven paddle. The size and shape of the paddle and the speed at which this mechanical stirrer is driven determine the efficiency of mixing.

Chemical engineers have developed a method of mixing which does away with the stirrer entirely. The technique, known as power fluidics, harnesses the forces generated by a moving liquid, such as the vortex, to control mixing. Vortex mixers work in a similar way to bath water flowing down a plug hole. The mixing action comes from the energy in the fluid as it is pumped in, and from the geometry of the system. The devices are very compact, with no internal moving parts to foul or corrode, important in the nuclear industry where the technology originated. Vortex mixers can give very tight control over fast reactions. That is why they are becoming favored for precipitation reactions where the mixing rate can be crucial to the size and shape of the solid which forms.

Power fluidics can do more than mix – it can control the flow of liquids and gases around the chemical plant. By a combination of geometry imposed by the fluidic devices and careful direction, the gas or process fluid is kept moving around the plant, starting, stopping, or diverting wherever it is needed. One of the first companies to endorse this fledgling technology publicly was pharmaceutical company SmithKline Beecham in 1992.

Right: An electron micrograph of a membrane surface which is used in water filtration.

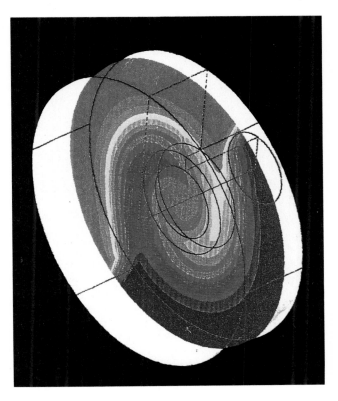

Above: A computer simulation of a vortex mixer at work, showing two chemicals – one blue and one red – being mixed.

Separation processes

Once a chemical reaction is complete the product must be separated from any unreacted starting material, reaction solvent, or unwanted by-products. Much of the plant in the chemical industry is used for the separation and purification of mixtures of compounds. In recent years market pressures have forced manufacturers to pay more attention to product quality. In the chemical industry, this is reflected in demands for purer products, often in circumstances where the quality of the raw materials is declining as the best

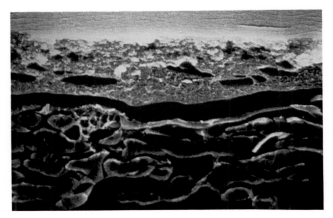

Left: A hazardous waste site in South Wales. The "end-of-pipe approach" in which waste is produced and then treated before disposal is now being replaced by more environmentally-friendly waste-minimization policies.

sources are exhausted – a squeeze from each end. In the U.S. increasing importance of separation has been recognized. Both the Amundsen Report and a report by the Department of Energy have emphasized the need to pay more attention to separation processes, whether using established or novel techniques.

In the 1990s the chemical industry is showing greater interest in using membranes to separate liquids from solids – in effect, mechanical filters which allow certain particles through while holding back others. The increased interest is because membranes offer several important advantages over competing separation techniques such as flocculation with vacuum filtration, centrifugation, sedimentation, evaporation, and ion exchange. The problem with these methods is that they usually cannot deal with particles smaller than 1 micron (1/25,000 in) and these are therefore either wasted

or contaminate the product. Membranes – made from a variety of polymeric materials, from polyethylene to cellulose acetate – have variable pore sizes so they can separate out these smaller particles. However, the size of the pores and the particles they filter cannot be directly linked. Other factors come into play to affect the permeability of the membrane, such as electrical repulsion when the particles and membrane are of the same charge.

Chemical engineers have therefore turned to ultrafiltration – the application of pressure or suction to force the solvent and small particles across the membrane while the larger particles are held back. The membrane is normally supported between fine wire screens or deposited in a highly porous support such as a sintered glass disc. Using such a system the liquid emerging from the membrane can be crystal clear and perfectly separated, with the advantage that the engineers can choose any pore size they please, from microns down to molecule-sized. Membranes can be made from a wide variety of materials, which means that there is usually one that is compatible with the chemicals being separated.

Membrane separations are, however, still quite expensive to use because the set-up costs of this new technology are high and the flow rate is comparatively small; consequently they are largely confined to high-value, low-volume processes. In

Left: Modern chemical production plants are highly complex sites with dozens of different processes, all vital to the end product, taking place. Chemical production in most modern plants is often controlled mostly or wholly by computers. This night-time view is of the Marchon chemical plant in the United Kingdom. The plant produces raw materials and intermediates for the detergent and toiletries industries.

Above: Plasma – the fourth state of matter – is playing an increasing role in chemical technology. This plasma flame has a temperature of 20,000 K.

Above right: This plant in the U.K., opened in 1992, uses a plasma in the manufacture of titanium dioxide by burning titanium tetrachloride in oxygen.

addition, membranes suffer from blocking of the pores and by themselves they cannot concentrate a slurry into a solid, because the feed material must remain watery. But scientists in the late 1980s found that by vibrating the membrane these problems could be solved. Shear waves produced by the membrane's vibrations cause solids to be repelled and liquid to flow to the pores unhindered. Vibrating membranes can also cope with more viscous feed material.

Separation processes are not an end in themselves and form part of closely linked production processes. Therefore they must be tailored to the total requirements of the process. Difficult separations can often be avoided by adjusting the conditions at an earlier stage. Concern about the environment has stimulated chemical engineers to recover materials rather than dispose of them, which would have contaminated the air, land, and water. But again, these problems can often be eliminated or reduced by designing processes in which effluent is reduced in quantity and toxicity.

Cutting down on waste

In the 1990s the most difficult problem facing the chemical industry will be what to do with its hazardous waste. The Environmental Protection Agency (EPA) has identified more than 1200 abandoned hazardous waste sites throughout the U.S.

for cleanup, and the status of tens of thousands more has yet to be decided. The cleanup operation is expected to cost over $100 billion by 2010. Immense pressure is being placed by government and public alike on industry to halt the flow of waste. This increased environmental awareness has stimulated many chemical companies to operate waste minimization policies. Indeed, such policies can now affect a company's very survival.

The future promises only increasingly stringent environmental regulations for the chemical industry. Treating waste after it is created – the so-called "end-of-pipe approach" – is not only expensive in both plant and operating costs, but also merely shifts the pollutant to another medium which has to be disposed of safely. Chemical engineers agree that the industry should stop producing waste, rather than produce it and then dispose of it. Effluent treatment is an admission of failure. But making a genuinely effluent-free process is going to be difficult.

Chemists and chemical engineers are studying many different ways of reducing waste. Solvents and unreacted starting materials are being recycled wherever possible. Reactor and stirrer design is being improved so that reactions are cleaner and better-yielding, hence producing fewer by-products. In some cases the waste by-product can only be avoided by using a completely different reaction. This will mean a change in the reactants used, different reaction chemistry, and, ultimately, a different process.

Perhaps the most powerful way to overcome

Right: Demonstration unit at the Indianapolis Power & Light Co., which uses a plasma to convert waste flue gases into ammonium nitrate fertilizer.

waste is improved instrumentation and increased automation. Here computer control has a major role to play.

Computers and chemicals

The chemical industry is one of the leaders in using computers to both reduce labor needs and maintain high quality and low costs. As the power of computers has grown and costs have tumbled, they have spread widely through all levels of the chemical process industries. Computer programs called distributed control systems have been written to control much of the operation of a chemical plant, such as opening and shutting valves and switching pumps and stirrers on and off. Other programs perform a host of important tasks around the plant but each works in isolation with limited scope for communication. Often a great deal of effort is needed to transfer information from one program to another. The program that controls the chemical plant, for example, is separate from another that needs the information from the first to help plan the schedules for the reactors, pumps, and other machinery.

Some time ago, plant managers set information technologists the task of allowing these different programs to share information more easily, to integrate them. The aim of this approach is computer integrated manufacturing, in which all the individual programs can be connected – from those that operate at the level of the plant to the accounting programs at a chemical company's head office. When full computer integration is achieved the chemical industry will be cleaner and safer, as well as more efficient.

Plasma processes

A new generation of plasma-based processes is set to take off in the chemical industry. Plasma is an ionized gas – a mixture of electrons, ions, and atoms. It is created at high temperatures (20,000 K for argon, for example) where collisions between atoms become violent enough to dislodge electrons, ionizing the atoms and altering the behavior of the gas so that it becomes a "fourth state of matter" – a plasma (see PLASMA PHYSICS).

The chemical industry's use of plasma has been somewhat limited so far. The world's second largest producer of titanium dioxide, Tioxide, uses plasma-based technology in the production of this widely used white pigment. The first experiments with plasma reactors took place as long ago as 1961. Companies were slow to adopt the technique: the first production plant was opened in 1971 and expanded in 1981. But in 1992 a second plant came on stream.

Plasma systems show great promise for development in incinerating hazardous waste and producing ceramic powders. The ceramic powder market is fairly small but could grow rapidly if ceramics become widely used in car engines, but the waste market also offers enormous potential.

Plasma for destroying waste is produced by heating a gas as it passes through an electric arc. Temperatures may reach 9032° F (5000° C). According to the gas chosen, the atmosphere of the plasma system will be oxidizing, to destroy organic wastes, or reducing, to melt scrap metal. Plasma arc systems have been tested and demonstrated to destroy PCBs and dioxins efficiently, to within Environmental Protection Agency standards.

Civil engineering

Civil engineers design and build roads and railroads and the structures associated with them, such as bridges and tunnels. They also have a wide role in the overall planning of transportation systems, and are responsibile for water supply, including the planning and construction of dams.

Today, more than ever before, when planning such schemes, civil engineers will be expected to demonstrate an awareness of environmental issues. They will have to work closely with scientists to prepare environmental impact assessments.

Bridges
Of all the projects in which civil engineers become involved, bridges are probably the most dramatic and prestigious.

During the 1990s a number of significant bridges are due for completion around the world. The record for the world's longest span, held since 1981 by Britain's Humber bridge with its 4625 ft (1410 m) main span, is set to be surpassed by a number of other structures. Denmark's Great Belt (Store Baelt) East bridge, which is part of an 11 mile (18 km) bridge and tunnel link between the islands of Zealand and Funen, will have a huge main span of 5330 ft (1624 m) and is expected to be completed in 1996 or 1997.

Only a year or two later this will be overtaken by the 6500 ft (1990 m) Akashi Kaikyo bridge in Japan, which spans the Akashi straits between the islands of Honshu and Shikoku. This bridge has been designed to withstand an earthquake measuring 8 on the Richter scale, but construction, which started in May 1988, is being complicated by the fact that this is an area of frequent typhoons.

Also in a typhoon area is Hong Kong's Tsing Ma bridge, part of the Lantau crossing serving the new airport. Its length will be slightly less than that of the Humber bridge. Unusually, road and rail traffic will be protected from typhoons inside the bridge's specially designed ventilated box-section deck. Six lanes of road traffic will also be carried on top. Construction started in 1992 and is set to proceed at a hectic pace, with the aim of being completed before Hong Kong reverts to Chinese rule in 1997.

Even longer bridges have been proposed elsewhere, but the only one currently at an advanced stage of planning is the Straits of Messina bridge in Italy, which would have a main span of 10,800 ft (3300 m).

Above: A computer illustration of the Akashi Kaikyo bridge across the Akashi straits in Japan. It will have the longest span in the world and towers almost as high as the Eiffel Tower.
Left: The bridge under construction. Typhoons often hit this area, adding to the construction difficulties.

Right: A micro-tunnelling machine, 10 ft (3 m) in diameter, used for creating sewage systems. It has a tungsten carbide cutter head which can be changed for a digging bucket (as here) according to the type of soil being bored. Workers digging the Channel tunnel use a massive cutter head, equipped with 85 tungsten carbide picks. This rotates at up to 4.5 revolutions per minute and advances in cuts that are 5 ft (1.5 m) deep. Each one of these cuts generates 86 tons of spoil, or excavated earth.

Rise of the cable-stayed bridge

All the examples mentioned so far have been suspension bridges, which have held a monopoly on the world's longest spans since the Brooklyn bridge was built in 1883. They consist of a high-strength steel cable hung between two towers and anchored to a heavy concrete block or to solid rock at each end. The bridge deck is hung from the main cables by suspender cables.

However, cable-stayed bridges have been increasing in popularity over the last two decades. In this type of bridge, the deck is supported by cables, usually in a fan-like arrangement, running diagonally from the deck to the towers. Cable-stayed bridges have only come into their own since computers became available to assist with the complex design calculations involved. The method of construction of this type of bridge leaves the deck more vulnerable to high winds in its partly complete state; this has also held back the length of span achieved.

The record span for a cable-stayed bridge has remained between 1300 ft and 1600 ft (400 m and 500 m) since the mid 1970s, the current record holder being the 1525 ft (465 m) Alex Fraser or Annacis bridge in Vancouver, Canada. Thus, the Pont de Normandie, currently being built between Le Havre and Honfleur in France with a main span of 2800 ft (853 m), represents a significant leap forward. It is due for completion in 1994. Its designers have dismissed suggestions that it will be very difficult to erect a stable deck of such a length.

Tunnels

Tunnels present civil engineers with perhaps the greatest challenges of their career. Even with the most detailed site investigation the danger of the tunnel face collapsing, or of a sudden inflow of water due to an unsuspected fissure, is always present to some extent.

In 1993 a long-standing goal of the tunneling industry will be achieved with the construction of the 30 mile (49 km) Channel tunnel between France and England. The project had been discussed for over a century, and started and abandoned on two occasions, before it became reality. Political rather than technical problems dogged the project: geological surveys had suggested at an early stage that the material under the Channel was chalk, a good tunneling material. Apart from some early problems on the French side, when unexpected fissures were met, this information proved largely correct.

The Channel tunnel is actually three parallel tunnels; two running tunnels will carry a high-speed rail track, one in each direction, with a service tunnel in between.

A recent development for tunneling in less than perfect ground conditions is the earth pressure balance tunneling machine. It was traditional practice when driving tunnels through water-logged ground to work in a compressed-air atmosphere to prevent water inundating the face. But workers under such conditions must observe strict decompression procedures to avoid injury, and, as more has been discovered about long-term adverse health effects, acceptable working pressures have been reduced.

The earth pressure balance machine eliminates the need for compressed air. Material excavated by its cutting head is fed by a screw conveyor through a bulkhead behind it, where it is taken up to the surface by belt conveyor. The solid plug of material in the screw conveyor supports the face and allows operators behind it to work in normal atmospheric pressure. Earth pressure balance machines are being used on the eastern tunnel of the Danish Store Baelt crossing, Europe's biggest construction project to date.

The New Austrian Tunneling Method

As a tunnel is excavated, a permanent lining, usually made of cast-iron or pre-cast concrete segments, is generally fixed in place to support the ground. However, increasing use is being made of the New Austrian Tunneling Method, especially for large diameter caverns. Sprayed concrete is used to line the tunnel immediately after excavation, followed by a secondary concrete lining applied later. Engineers monitor the sprayed concrete lining for movement and if necessary they can increase its thickness.

Because the initial lining can be formed very quickly, there is less risk to workers from a collapse of the face or from settlement at ground level, which would also lead to the danger of damage to existing buildings.

Transportation

Tunnels and bridges are usually constructed as part of road or rail links, and civil engineers are heavily involved in the wider picture of transportation planning. Rail has been enjoying something of a revival in recent years after being eclipsed by road for most of the century. France, Germany, and Spain are all building new high-speed rail links and a Europe-wide network is being discussed.

The French TGV (*Train à Grand Vitesse*) is typical: it carries passengers at 188 mph (300 km/h) and has proved able to compete with internal air flights. The special track which allows the TGV to operate at full speed currently runs from Paris to Lyon, Le Mans, and Tours. Another line, TGV Nord, to connect with the Channel tunnel and Brussels, is well advanced, as is TGV Interconnexion, a ring service running round Paris. TGV Provençale, running south from Lyon, is currently also being planned.

Less glamorously, there has been a huge revival of interest in rail-based solutions to urban traffic congestion, particularly in the older crowded city areas. More and more experts are convinced that building roads to accommodate predicted levels of traffic merely causes the predictions to fulfill themselves, so the emphasis is increasingly turning toward encouraging people to use public transportation whenever possible.

Water supply

Improvements in the public health of the developed world last century owed as much to civil engineers providing sanitation and clean drinking water as to advances in medical science. Providing adequate water of a similarly high standard in developing countries remains a major concern.

Water supply is causing concern in the developed world, too, for a variety of reasons. Increasing levels of pollutants, particularly nitrates from agricultural fertilizers, coupled with increasingly stringent health standards, means that water supply companies need to invest in more sophisticated treatment plants before they deliver water to customers.

Even well-established treatment techniques have recently begun to be called into question for a variety of health reasons. Water engineers have long seen chlorine as offering the ideal way of killing water-borne bacteria because it remains effective after the water leaves the treatment

Far left: One of the 16 foot (4.8 m) diameter tunneling machines for the 30 mile (49 km) Channel Tunnel, due for completion in 1993
Left: The Pont de Normandie across the Seine estuary in France, which will be the longest cable-stayed bridge in the world, under construction.

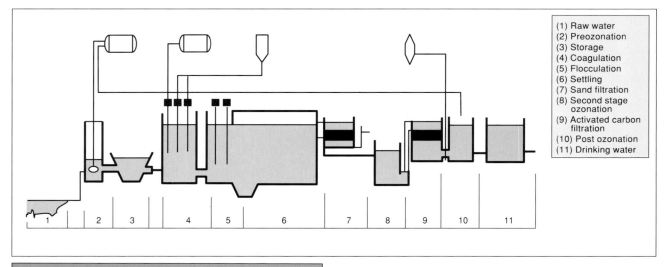

(1) Raw water
(2) Preozonation
(3) Storage
(4) Coagulation
(5) Flocculation
(6) Settling
(7) Sand filtration
(8) Second stage ozonation
(9) Activated carbon filtration
(10) Post ozonation
(11) Drinking water

• FACT FILE •

- Bridge spans have increased in length by a factor of 3.5 every 100 years since 1770. Longer bridges have been made possible by the development of new materials, such as wrought iron in the 1800s, steel later in the same century, and high-strength steel in the 1930s. These materials gave progressively greater strength with less weight.

- Before the Humber bridge in England took the record for the world's longest span in 1981, it had been held for 17 years by the 4250 ft (1295 m) Verrazano Narrows bridge, New York. It has two decks and is still probably the world's heaviest bridge.

- New fiber-reinforced plastics offer the possibility of even longer spans – as much as 5 miles (8 km), say experts. So far, however, the use of such materials in civil engineering has been limited to secondary structures such as gantries for freeway signs or maintenance decks under an existing bridge.

- What is thought to be the world's first plastic bridge, a cable-stayed footbridge with a modest 200 ft (61 m) main span, was built at Aberfeldy, Scotland, in 1992. Apart from its foundations, it is completely made of composite plastics: cellular glass-fiber-reinforced polyester for the deck and "Aramid" cables. This project should stimulate considerable interest in the use of such new materials.

Above: An ozone water treatment plant. Environmental engineers are predicting a move away from chlorine – currently used to disinfect about half of U.S. water supplies – to ozonation, used in France for nearly a century.

plant. However, recent studies have shown that some upland water sources contain organic substances which react with chlorine to form compounds called trihalomethanes. Research in the U.S. has linked these substances with certain forms of cancer. Accordingly, alternative disinfectants such as ozone, which is already widely used in France, are increasingly gaining favor. Because ozone has no residual effect, however, some chlorine still has to be added to the water in order to provide a satisfactory level of protection in the distribution pipes.

Above: Civil engineers are also involved in the construction of railway tracks, such as the special ones built for the TGV in France.

Climatology

Climatology, the study of past, present, and future climates, has become of vital public interest in recent years. An issue that captured general attention in the early 1980s was the "nuclear winter" theory: that the explosion of large numbers of nuclear weapons would create vast clouds of dust and smoke that would blanket a large portion of the world. Some scientists calculated that this thick pall would persist for so long, and absorb so much of the Sun's heat, that surface temperatures in continental interiors would drop by perhaps as much as 36-54° F (20-30° C). This would have catastrophic effects for nearly all forms of life on Earth. The temperature drop and loss of sunlight would cause plants and the animals dependent on them, including ourselves, to suffer a drastic decline or even become extinct.

The present consensus among climatologists is that the effects of nuclear winter would not be as severe as first feared. The threat of nuclear war also seems to have receded. But the work of climatologists has become even more important with the discovery of other potentially disastrous environmental effects, such as global warming, the attendant rise in sea levels, and ozone thinning (see ENVIRONMENTAL SCIENCE). There is also a wide range of more localized effects, some natural and some caused by human activities, which could

have profound consequences for agriculture. The ability to predict such changes would give policymakers the chance to avert them or, where they could not do this, give plant breeders time to develop new varieties and farmers time to adapt their methods.

Climatology programs

Climatologists have had an inkling of some of these problems for many years, and the World Meteorological Organization (WMO) set up the World Climate Program (WCP) in 1979. Among other investigations, WCP includes the World Ocean Circulation Experiment, a seven-year project that began in 1990 and was designed to make best use of the European Space Agency's ERS-1 satellite, launched in May 1991, which is specifically designed to monitor the oceans.

With the upsurge in public and political concern in the 1980s, WMO and the United Nations Environment Program (UNEP) set up the Intergovernmental Panel on Climate Change (IPCC) in 1988. The IPCC's first Science Assessment was issued in 1990. In addition, the WMO and other international scientific unions were establishing the Global Climate Observing System (GCOS).

Some human activities have almost immediate effects on regional climate. Deforestation, for example, is now known to cause a greater amount of sunlight to be reflected back from the ground,

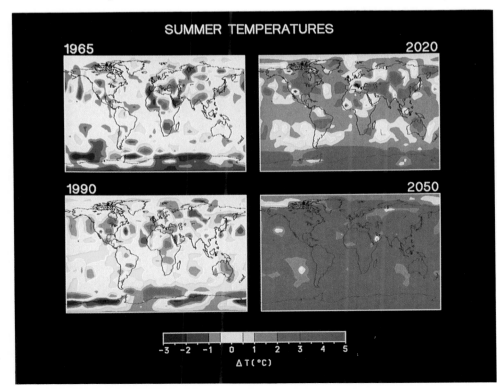

Left: Computer predictions showing past and projected global surface air temperatures. Red and orange indicate increased temperatures. The data come from NASA's Global Climate Model using the assumption that emissions of green houses gases will increase at present rates.

Above: The world's oldest roadway, the Sweet Track in Somerset, England, has timbers preserved from 3806 BC. Beside it were the remains of beetles which can only exist in a warmer climate than found in Britain today, giving clues to climate change.

Above: Scientists at a conference in Zimbabwe gather on the dried-up bed of Darwendale Reservoir in 1992, in an area which should be submerged. Water shortages have hit many countries, including even some with normally wet climates, such as Britain and New Zealand.

with a resulting decrease in surface heating and a reduction in rainfall. This process undoubtedly changed the climate over large areas of the Near and Middle East in prehistoric times, and is suspected to have made a significant contribution to the decline of various early civilizations.

Determining past climates

It is essential to discover whether the apparent climatic changes that we see around the world are really permanent, or are simply temporary fluctuations from some overall, long-term average. For

example, we must expect occasional long runs of years that are particularly hot and dry, like those that occurred over much of the Northern Hemisphere in the late 1980s.

This has given added urgency to the study of climates over long stretches of time, both in historical times and at earlier geological periods (where the discipline becomes known as paleoclimatology). If scientists can determine the range and duration of long-term climatic fluctuations it should help them to predict what will happen in future, provided – and this is a very important

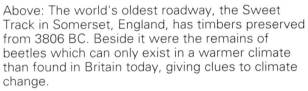

Left: The "Iceman" found in 1991 in the Alps between Austria and Italy had been preserved in the ice for 4000 years. His body yielded clues to the climate during the Bronze Age when he lived.

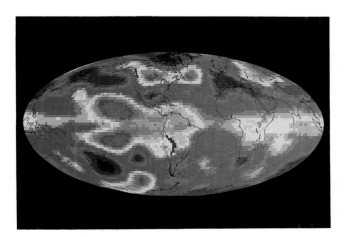

Left: Satellite images keep track of the Antarctic ice cover. This infrared view, taken in January 1992, shows a 75 mile (120 km) iceberg at center left.
Right: Temperature anomaly map of the globe, using data from the TIROS-N weather satellite, shows an El Niño event in progress.

proviso – that they truly understand the underlying mechanisms at work.

Many different types of material provide information about past climate. Historical records are an obvious source, but there are many other types of evidence. Ancient bodies can be preserved in peat bogs, as Tollund Man was in Denmark and Lindow Man was in Britain (see ARCHAEOLOGY). Rarely, one may be found in a glacier, as "Iceman" was in the Alps in 1991. Study of clothing and other items, or sometimes even the remnants of the person's final meal, gives valuable clues about the plants (and thus the climate) in the area at the time. The stomach contents of frozen mammoths discovered in Siberia have been used for the same purpose. The oldest known roadway gives evidence about the climate prevailing around 4000 BC, the time it was constructed. This is the Sweet Track, found in an English peat bog. The fossilized remnants of a particular form of beetle were found alongside the wooden walkway. Such beetles exist only where summers are about 3-5° F (2-3° C) warmer and winters 3-7° F (2-4° C) colder than those found in southern England today.

Other major techniques include DENDROCHRONOLOGY, the study of tree-rings. The thickness of a ring indicates the temperature and rainfall in a particular year. Pollen analysis shows the prevalence of particular species in the past, which gives an idea of the prevailing climate.

Ice ages

Studies of past climate have revealed that, although many climatic changes take decades or centuries to become established, sudden alterations can occur when the whole climate switches from one stable state to another. Ice ages, for example, appear to begin and end very rapidly, perhaps over no more than 50 years. Overall, ice ages have two main contributory factors: Milankovitch cycles, which are regular changes in the direction of the Earth's axis of rotation and changes in its orbit around the Sun; and geological changes, particularly continental drift. When (as at present) land masses surround or cover the poles, they prevent warm ocean waters from reaching them, thus giving rise to ice caps. This occurs rarely, so that, taken over the whole of geological time, ice ages are infrequent events.

The evidence suggests that, ignoring any disturbing effects caused by human activities, the likely climate in the next century or so would be like that prevailing in the "Little Ice Age" (approximately 1550-1850), when average temperatures were about 2-5° F (1-3° C) lower than now. Although over the last 11,500 years we have been living in a warm interglacial period, in the longer term (over the next few thousand years), a return to true ice-age conditions would be expected in the Northern Hemisphere.

El Niño

But successful predictions require appropriate computer models of individual climatic systems (see also METEOROLOGY). In recent years, climatologists have discovered an important process, the El Niño-Southern Oscillation (ENSO), and have made great progress in modeling it.

Off the west coast of South America, the winds are normally westward-blowing, and cause water to move away from the coast, producing an upwelling of cold, nutrient-rich waters, supporting large fish stocks. But every four to seven years there is a failure of the fisheries, accompanying a reversal of the wind direction and increased rainfall in the area. This is El Niño, and it normally lasts about a year.

Climatologists now know that this is only one feature of an ENSO event, which disrupts oceanic and atmospheric circulation over a large portion of the globe. High pressure builds up over the western tropical Pacific, and eastward-blowing winds spread a broad tongue of warm surface water towards the east. There is a decrease in rainfall

Left: Preparing a 17th-century lead coffin in St Mary's City, MD, for extraction of the air possibly sealed inside in colonial days, with the aim of analyzing pre-industrial air samples.
Above: Work in progress to extract air samples from lead coffins. The "glove box" is flooded with argon gas to protect possible 17th-century air within the coffins from contamination.

over the western Pacific, Indonesia, and Australia. The circulation over the Indian Ocean and the rest of the Southern Hemisphere is also disrupted. A prolonged ENSO event in 1991-2 produced droughts in Brazil, Australia, and, with devastating effect, vast areas of southern Africa. Although the precise connections are uncertain, it appears that ENSO effects are linked to weather patterns north of the equator. Pressure drops over the north-eastern Pacific, and in 1991-2 this produced greatly increased rainfall and flooding along the west coast of North America and in Texas.

There are several computer models of the ENSO, and they show some success in predicting its severity and duration, but not yet its timing, nor that of the "cold" event (sometimes called "La Niña") that follows it, and which may also have severe effects. Although a few experts argue that ENSO events are initiated by major volcanic eruptions, this theory is not accepted by most climatologists. With such work, climatologists are gradually approaching their ultimate goal of predicting future climate.

Unfortunately, the inadequacy of current models – particularly in the way they handle processes involving moisture – means that, although there is general agreement that some degree of global warming is likely to occur, we are unable to predict the amount of change, or its precise timing, or the relation of these to the anticipated Milankovitch cooling.

Data from the dead

In October 1992, after extensive preparations, work began on recovering atmospheric samples from a very unlikely source. In 1989, investigations with ground-penetrating radar at St. Mary's City in Maryland found three sealed lead coffins beneath the ruins of a church. The coffins are thought to be those of the family of Governor Philip Calvert, and would therefore date from around 1680.

Scientists have often tried to obtain air samples dating from before the industrial revolution, when pollution began to increase. Air trapped inside amber (fossilized tree resin) has been used to determine the atmospheric composition at the time of fossilization. Unfortunately, the amount of air obtained has been very small, making analysis difficult, and the uncertainty is increased by changes in composition that occur as gases diffuse into the amber. The larger samples from the lead coffins should make the task easier, and the three sets of results may be checked against one another.

It should be possible to obtain precise details of any change in trace gases such as nitrous oxide, which is not altered by the human remains in the coffins, and is not produced by their decomposition. Such information is particularly important because nitrous oxide is a major product of industrialization and is implicated in the greenhouse effect. The results should also be a useful check on the findings from bubbles trapped in ice cores.

Computer science

No area of science or technology is changing as fast as computer science. It is said that if the car industry had progressed the way the computer industry has in the past 20 years, a Rolls Royce would now go a million miles an hour, get about a million miles a gallon, and cost about 50 cents.

The mass market

The early 1990s have seen massive changes in the products available. The biggest development has been the concerted move away from command line interfaces; that is, systems where users had to type specific strings of characters to get the computer to work.

The replacement, made possible by the huge jump in computing power available on the desktop, is graphical user interfaces (GUIs). With these, users navigate the on-screen windows and icons using a pointing device such as a mouse. The original GUI was developed at Xerox's PARC research center. From there, it was picked up by Apple Computer for its Macintosh and it has since been widely copied. Now, almost every desktop computer follows this pattern.

Graphical interfaces open up a range of applications, such as desktop publishing and presentation graphics, which depend on the user's ability to manipulate images directly. At the same time, new input and storage devices have broadened the range of what a computer can handle. "Multimedia" computers have the ability to record, play back, and edit sounds, full motion video, and photographic images.

These advances are the result of increasingly powerful microprocessors. As a rough estimate, the power that can be crammed into a box that fits on a desktop doubles about every year, while the prices keep going down. But more powerful chips do not just mean more powerful computers. Micro-processors are used to control almost every appliance these days, from VCRs to washing machines to automobiles. As a result, several companies are working on common standards for single-purpose chips, so that these could be used to create so-called "intelligent buildings" (see BUILDING CON-

Above: The Touchstone Delta computer, one of a series of powerful supercomputers developed by Intel. It uses parallel processing, once regarded as a curiosity best suited to research into artificial intelligence but now becoming important for many computing applications .
Right: A RISC (Reduced Instruction Set Computer) chip, such as those used in the Touchstone Delta. RISC chips are designed to handle commonly used instructions at very high speeds.

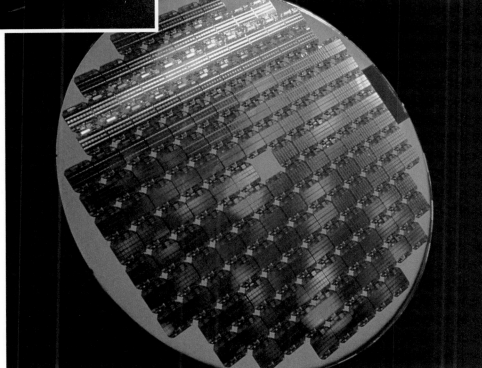

Above: A virtual reality (VR) image of the Earth's terrain, showing both the surface and the ocean floor in three dimensions. Grid data were mathematically transformed to form the globe shape. Warped grids were deformed to create three-dimensional surfaces which were then overlaid with a map and artificial coloring to indicate altitude and depth.

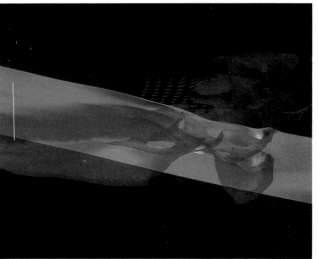

Above: A virtual reality simulation of a thunderstorm. This image combines data on cloud water density (shown as a translucent blue surface), wind direction, and magnitude (shown as red arrows of varying lengths and directions). Temperature values are shown as different colors on the blue plane which is cutting through the base of the storm.

STRUCTION), where all the individual systems can be programmed using one remote control.

Display technology is also taking a leap forward with Thin Film Transistor, or active matrix, color screens. The smallest versions of these are already familiar in tiny portable TVs. Larger ones, such as those appearing on notebook computers, are still difficult and expensive to produce, because making them involves laying down one million transistors. Nonetheless, the technology is seen as the future of both computer and TV screens.

Supercomputers

There are two ways of defining a supercomputer. The first is by hardware: a supercomputer is the fastest computer on the planet. Some claim that at the moment this is the Touchstone Delta, a prototype built in early 1991 by Intel, in use at Pasadena's California Institute of Technology. The second is by the ability to accomplish large volumes of computing. However, there are tasks that defeat even the largest and fastest computers today. These are the so-called Grand Challenges of computing, such as global climate modeling, the analysis and modeling of ground waters and atmosphere, and modeling vehicle dynamics, virus structures, semiconductors, and superconductors.

Other projects already under way also require massive amounts of computational strength, such as the project to map the human genome (see GENETICS). The Delta uses a principle that many

believe is the future of supercomputing: parallel computing. Traditional "vector" computers have one very large processor optimized to do very fast calculations concerned with one problem at a time. In contrast, the Delta is made up of 520 Intel i860 RISC chips, plus about 50 ordinary 386 chips – the type used in everyday PCs. Even the disk drives are off-the-shelf components. Such a computer can carry out many different tasks at the same time in order to achieve its goal.

This approach has a huge advantage in terms of speed of development and ease and cost of maintenance – more processors or disk drives can be added whenever more power or storage is needed. The RISC chips themselves are new developments. These are chips that derive their speed from being optimized to execute the most commonly used instructions. Their name derives from Reduced Instruction Set Computer.

The big difficulty with a parallel-processing computer is programming it – the job must be split up into processor-sized chunks. This works well for some things: image processing, say, or virtual reality applications, where different processors can work on different groups of pixels or different modules, such as sound, graphics, or communications. For scientific applications, where there are long strings of numbers that have to be added or multiplied and each result depends on the result calculated before it, however, this approach will not work. Even so, parallel processing is important in

Right and inset: Many properties of molecules stem from their shape and ability to match receptors on other molecules – this is how viruses manage to infect cells, for example. So chemists are now using VR to experiment with choosing the right molecular arrangement to fit into a given structure. The system also displays structures in three dimensions rather than simply on a flat screen.

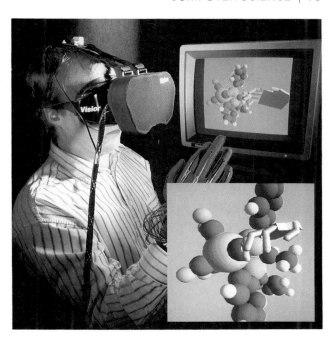

research work on optical computers – which use light pulses sent down fiber-optic cables instead of electrons sent down wires – which could replace the electronic machines in use today.

Virtual reality

More and more powerful computers mean more and more data. Many applications, such as corporate information systems, scientific studies of fluid dynamics, and weather forecasting, generate more data than humans can understand or assimilate directly. One solution is to present data as pictures which can display the data so it can be comprehended at a glance.

Visualization, however, uses only one of the five senses. Virtual reality uses touch and hearing, as well. The computer-generated image is viewed through a headset with a monitor screen for each eye, giving a 3D view, and the user may wear gloves containing position sensors so the computer is aware of the wearer's hands. This allows the user to interact with the computer. As well as its use in games, serious research is going on. At IBM's Thomas J. Watson Research Center, for example, an attempt is being made to incorporate the laws of physics – friction, gravity, and so on – into the world of virtual reality.

Incorporating the physical laws will eventually allow applications like simulating the airflow on airplane wings in test situations in real time, or docking molecules, or trying out new surgical operations (see ANATOMY AND SURGERY). Sound is already being used in multimedia applications. Force feedback (the sense of touch), though, is also needed. In applications such as the University of North Carolina's experiments in molecular docking, where biochemists try to determine whether a drug molecule fits well into a protein molecule, force feedback helps the biochemist judge the fit. The process is similar to piecing together a broken

Right: Software developed by IBM in the United Kingdom can now translate photographic images into three-dimensional models. In this image, a pencil sharpener has been photographed dozens of times at ten degree angles. Once the images have been assimilated by the computer, it produces an identical set of pictures which can be used to compare its model to the real thing.

plate by wiggling the pieces against each other to feel for the best fit.

All sorts of uses for virtual reality are already being found. At NASA's Ames Research Center, scientists can explore the surface of Mars in this way. IBM is working with Chrysler and Boeing on applications to speed low-cost dashboard and cockpit design. Silicon Graphics, famous for making the workstations on which the special effects for the movie *Terminator 2* were designed, has a system which the urban planners for Los Angeles are using to model their plans for renovating the areas damaged by the 1992 riots.

Telecommunications

Along with the rise in computing power have come increasing links between computers and TELECOMMUNICATIONS, an area which loosely includes everything from local area networks covering a single business to the world's largest electronic network, Internet, which has an estimated four million users at government and academic institutions worldwide.

As everything from words to color photographs becomes digital, transmission over the telephone lines becomes the most logical way of moving such data around. High-speed connections are now available using satellite links and fast modems (which link computers with phone lines).

Artificial Intelligence

There was much excitement toward the end of 1991 when the program *PC Therapist*, a program that asks questions and makes responses that imitate those of a psychiatrist, passed a limited version of the Turing Test; that is, its responses could not be distinguished from those of a human. At the same time, games-playing computers are beginning to challenge the human masters. The most advanced computer chess program, *Deep Thought*, has beaten some of the lower ranked grandmasters. The most advanced checkers program, *Chinook*, earned itself the world number two ranking and the right to challenge the (human) world champion. The match was played in September, 1992; the machine lost.

Games-playing machines – and other types of rule-based expert systems in areas like medicine – tend to rely on large databases of possible positions and legal moves by weeding out losing sequences. As an approach to intelligence, this is limited: the machines can add to their databases, but they cannot "learn" in any human sense of the word. What makes the human brain powerful is not its processing speed, but the number of processors (neurons) and their interconnectedness. This is mimicked by neural networks, originally developed in the 1950s and 1960s and now in a revival which is fueled, at least partly, by the easy availability of cheaper, more powerful processors and memory. Neural networks can be software, hardware, or a combination of the two. They are, along with other techniques like genetic algorithms, an attempt to use our increased understanding of how brains work in designing faster and more flexible computer systems.

Techniques like these are important in optimization problems such as job scheduling or finding the best route for a traveling salesperson. They are also needed in systems where flexibility and adaptability are needed, such as speech and handwriting recognition.

Above: So-called "flash chips" such as these are now replacing conventional hard drives in portable computers and can also provide a large memory in such devices as telephones and sound recorders.

• FACT FILE •

- The use of computers for animating movies is at the forefront of computer applications because the financial return on a box office smash hit pays for development work that could otherwise take years to reap a reward.

- While computers can be used to manipulate images and to add color, perhaps the greatest potential comes from computer-generated images (CGI) – producing a complete and realistic image totally within the computer. At the moment this is restricted to movie work only, where there is no limit on the time taken to produce one image. Eventually, however, improved computer speeds will mean that the images produced by CGI and virtual reality will merge.

- Already, scenes are being produced where "extras" are generated by the computer. *Batman Returns* was an early example in which thousands of bats and penguins were computer-generated, each programmed with information on how to move and how to avoid impossible situations. The images were then allowed to interact among themselves. In the meantime, computer animated films are achieving increasing reality. Experts suggest that before long, even lead actors could be replaced by CGI.

Condensed matter physics

At one time the words "solid-state" on a hi-fi unit showed that it used what was then the latest in technology: transistors and other semiconductors, rather than the old vacuum tubes used for many years. In fact, solid-state physics is one part of what is now called condensed matter physics, which looks at the properties and behavior of many materials, both solid and liquid, though there has been vastly more work over the years on solids than on liquids.

The variety of solid materials is incredibly wide and includes metals, semiconductors, insulators or dielectrics, molecular materials, and even solidified gases such as dry ice. The materials may be organic or inorganic, elements, alloys, and compounds, and include the important polymers which have supplanted metals and metal alloys in much of daily life and increasingly in high technology applications.

Clearly, many materials can exist in both solid and liquid states, depending on temperature; if a liquid is cooled suddenly it may be frozen into a solid in which the atoms or ions are arranged in an essentially random manner. Such materials are described as *non-crystalline* or *amorphous* and include such everyday materials as window glass. The majority of materials, however, are *crystalline* and are composed of three-dimensional arrays of atoms or ions. Many materials may be prepared in the form of single or nearly perfect crystals, or as polycrystalline aggregates which consist of crystalline grains. Alternatively, many materials can be prepared as thin films, either crystalline or amorphous, between 10 to 5000 nanometers in thickness – for comparison, the wavelength of yellow light is about 500 nm. Such films have been developed in recent years as components of electronic microcircuits, for protective coatings on solid materials, for optical waveguides, and for many other purposes.

Condensed matter is usually studied by observing and measuring such properties as the material's structural, magnetic, mechanical, optical, and electrical characteristics. This usually begins by preparing samples of very high purity and crystalline perfection, so that they can be compared with more normal materials. This reveals the effects of the impurities and defects which are usually present. In fact, in many non-metallic materials it is often the defects and impurities which give them their properties, but even with these materials the electrical properties at very low temperatures are controlled by imperfections. The addition

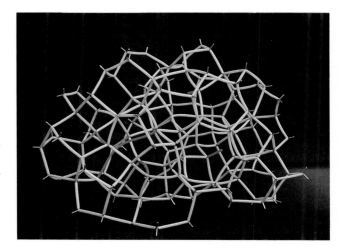

Above: Amorphous silicon still has a tetrahedral structure but does not repeat regularly. This alters the mobility of electrons in the material.

of a few per cent of carbon and chromium to iron, for example, turns it into steel with very different properties from normal soft iron.

Seeing atoms

Traditional studies of structures of condensed matter were made using X-ray and electron CRYSTALLOGRAPHY and, since the 1950s the scanning electron microscope. This has made it possible to watch small solid-state devices while they are operating and to examine the tiny structures used in microelectronics. But in the last decade new methods of improving these analytical techniques have reached a stage of very high sophistication, so that structural features the size of individual atoms or ions can be seen.

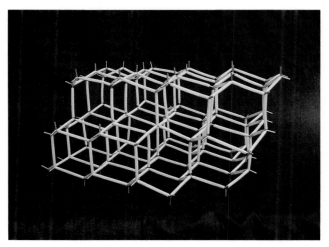

Above: The normal crystalline structure of silicon, in which each Si atom is surrounded by four others in a regularly repeating tetrahedral arrangement.

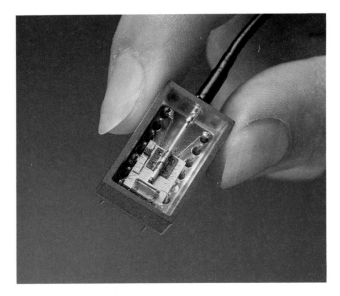

Above: Inside a semiconductor laser, now widely used for optical fiber communications and in such devices as CD players
Below: A scanning tunneling microscope at the Cavendish Laboratory, Cambridge, UK. The microscope has a special head unit developed in collaboration with W A Technology Ltd that allows measurements to be made with atomic resolution down to within a few degrees of absolute zero. The microscope unit is housed in the small cryostat visible just behind the operator.

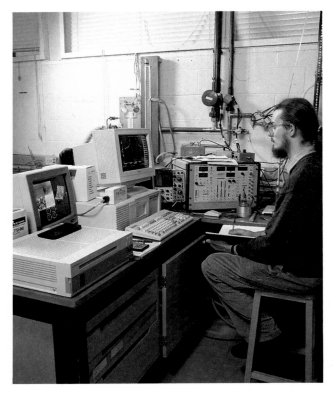

A recent instrument for studying fine surface features of condensed matter, the *scanning tunneling microscope* (STM), has become very popular. The STM works on a principle completely different from a conventional or electron microscope. In effect, rather than "seeing" an object, it "feels" it, using an extremely fine pointed probe with a tip which may be only a single atom across. The probe does not actually touch the surface but remains a few atom-diameters above it. A voltage applied between the tip and the surface produces a flow of electrons between the two which can be measured as a current. The tip is scanned over the surface to keep the electron flow constant, and in doing so traces out the surface's profile.

Scans using an STM are then converted by a computer into images which reveal atoms and molecules on the surface. The arrangement of the atoms can therefore be mapped directly, and any variations in the surface are immediately visible.

An adaptation of the STM is the atomic force microscope (ATM). In this case the tip actually rests on the surface of the material and the arrangement of atoms on the surface is detected by the movements of the tip, like the stylus of a phonograph record.

Researchers exploring the possibilities of these devices have produced tiny messages by gouging out grooves in the arrangements of atoms, or by applying a voltage to the tip that causes atoms to detach from the tip and deposit themselves on the surface. The "message" written in this way can even be erased by applying an opposite voltage, which causes the deposited atoms to fly back to the tip again. While the messages written in this way have no serious content, the power of the technique was demonstrated in 1991 by a researcher at the University of Basel, Switzerland, who wrote the word "Heureka" between the individual pits of a compact disc – up to now, one of the densest storage mediums available! The method is currently very costly and slow, but there are hopes that in the future it could form the basis of a workable data storage medium.

The deposition method, if refined and speeded up, could be used to draw the ultimate in miniature circuits. At the University of Texas at Austin, Alex de Lozanne has deposited a line of nickel only 50 nanometers wide. But exceeding even this in miniature components, a switch has been created consisting of a single xenon atom which can be in one of two stable positions. The potential for moving individual atoms around using STM devices is still being explored.

Amorphous materials

Two decades ago, amorphous materials were virtually unheard of. Today, however, they are of major

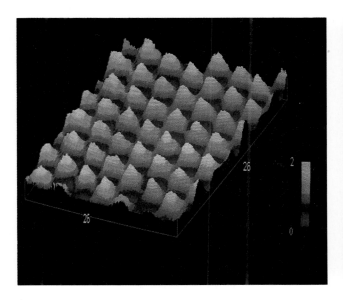

Above: A perspective image of the surface of crystalline graphite, showing clearly the hexagonal arrangement of carbon atoms in the surface. The area shown is 200 times smaller than the wavelength of light – the colors shown are false.

Above: A range of solar panels made from amorphous silicon. Additional applications of this material are still being developed.

importance. In a crystal there is a regular arrangement of atoms or ions in three directions so that the arrangements around all atoms of a particular kind are similar, i.e., the crystal possesses short-range order. Furthermore, if we progress in regular steps along a row of ions in the crystal, we can predict from the uniformity of the spacing when we shall expect to find the next one, i.e., the crystal also possesses long-range order. In an amorphous material, which may include glasses and thin non-crystalline dielectric or semiconducting films, the long-range order is destroyed and the short-range order is retained, albeit with some distortion.

The interest in modern glass physics was stimulated by work in Russia on glassy semiconducting compounds based on selenium and tellurium, and by the discovery in an industrial laboratory in the U.K. that phosphate glasses containing transition metal ions behaved as electronic semiconductors, in some ways similar to silicon. Theoretical work in the U.S. and U.K. in particular led to a much improved understanding of the band structure of glasses, of their optical transmitting properties, and of their electrical characteristics. The results have had an impact on technology. Optical glass fibers for communications, solar cells made from amorphous silicon diodes (as used, for example, in some pocket calculators), and improved laser materials have all been developed into usable devices.

One application of amorphous materials is for *memory switches*. These use a thin layer of glass containing such materials as copper phosphate or silicon-tellurium-arsenic-germanium, known as STAG. The glass is usually no more than 5-20 micrometers thick, and has metal electrodes deposited on either side in a vacuum chamber, creating a metal-glass-metal sandwich. This forms the memory switch.

At low voltages and very small currents, the switch is off – that is, current passes through the glass according to the classic Ohm's Law, which says that current increases as the voltage does. But above a critical voltage the current suddenly rises and the resistance of the sandwich to current drops dramatically – from perhaps thousands of megohms to just a few tens of ohms. The switch is now on and remains so, even if the voltage drops to zero. To turn it off again it needs a high-current pulse. At the moment the device is limited to about 100 million operations before it fails, and it has not yet found a commercial application.

High temperature superconductors

Some metals and alloys completely lose their electrical resistance at a well-defined *transition temperature*. This is called *superconduction*. They can be almost perfectly diamagnetic – that is, the superconductivity can prevent the penetration of magnetic fields. This makes certain superconducting materials very useful for making the windings of very strong electromagnets without needing enormous power, while the lack of resistance avoids overheating.

Originally, it seemed that the transition tem-

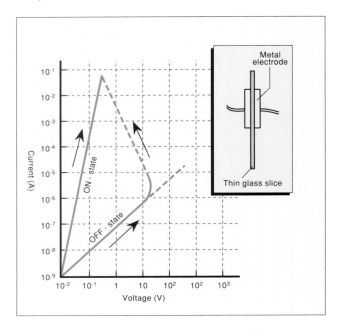

Above: How a memory switch works. At low power (OFF) the switch behaves normally. But at a certain point much more current can suddenly flow and the switch turns ON.

perature would always be very low. Before 1986 one of the highest transition temperatures was about 20 K for an alloy of niobium, aluminum, and germanium. But then Bednorz and Müller in Switzerland showed that in certain ceramic materials with a deformed perovskite structure, the transition temperature was higher. Subsequently, heat-treated materials composed of yttrium, barium, copper, and oxygen have given transition temperatures greater than 90 K. Japanese researchers announced in 1992 that a superconductor made of copper oxide, strontium, and calcium is superconducting at 170 K. This is still low compared with everyday conditions, but it is well above the temperature of readily available liquid nitrogen (77 K), so these new superconductors are much easier to use than metallic ones.

While these materials have already found their way into practical applications, such as body scanners and generators (see ELECTRICAL ENGINEERING), researchers are trying to achieve even higher transition temperatures. The ultimate goal would be a cheap superconducting material which works at room temperature, making electrical transmission losses virtually zero. Whether this can ever be achieved remains to be seen.

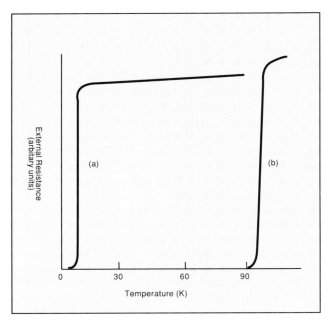

Above: Superconductors suddenly lose their resistance at a transition temperature. Material A only superconducts at a few degrees above zero, but B remains superconducting at a much higher temperature.
Left: A low-temperature superconducting magnet in the course of manufacture. The advent of high-temperature superconductors will enable such magnets to become much more compact.

Cosmology

Cosmology is the study of the origin of the universe and how it changes as time passes. This involves trying to explain the structure of the universe as we see it today, to describe how it was in the past, and to predict what might happen in the distant future. Attempts to answer these questions have led to the proposal of many different cosmological models or theories. New instruments, such as the Hubble Space Telescope, are providing information which may change our ideas radically (see ASTROPHYSICS). Observations are made of distant galaxies – huge groupings of stars – or quasars, which are believed to be galaxies with intensely bright cores, mostly very remote.

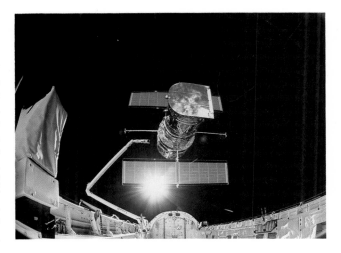

Above: The launch of the Hubble Space Telescope from the space shuttle provided an important new tool in cosmological research. Its main mirror lies within the tube, here closed off by a cover in which a reflection of Earth's surface is seen.

The rate of expansion and age of the universe

The currently favored cosmological model is the hot Big Bang theory. According to this, the universe was created from an unbelievably hot, superdense state in a single instant, between 10 and 20 billion years ago, and is presently expanding.

In the 1920s Edwin Hubble found that in all distant galaxies the lines in their optical spectra were shifted towards the red. Today most astronomers support Hubble's interpretation that each galaxy, or cluster of galaxies, is receding from every other one at speeds proportional to their distances. If the galaxies are moving apart now, they must have been very close together at some time in the past. This idea is at the center of the Big Bang theory. The relationship between speed of recession and distance is known as Hubble's Law, and the factor linking the two is called Hubble's constant.

Hubble's constant is not known as precisely as astronomers would like, but probably lies between 40 and 80 kilometers per second per megaparsec (km/s/Mpc) – that is, a galaxy one million parsecs (3.26 million light years) away has a redshift of 40 to 80 km/s. This implies that the age of the universe is between 10 and 20 billion years. The reason these figures are so uncertain is that it is hard to measure the distances of remote galaxies, and different methods give different results.

Support for the Big Bang theory comes from measurements which show that helium is the second most abundant element in the universe after hydrogen. The amount seems too great to have been produced by the nuclear processes occurring in stars which transform hydrogen into helium.

Right: Detail of part of the Virgo cluster of galaxies, which is the nearest supercluster to our own group. The small, round images are nearby stars in our own galaxy, but the larger fuzzy images are other galaxies in the cluster.

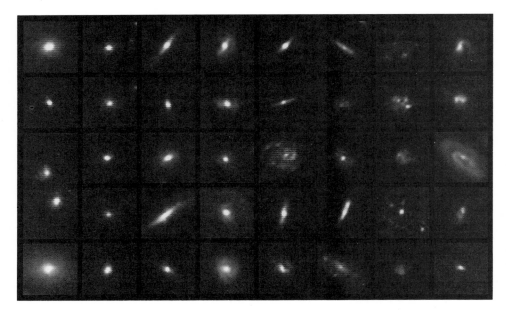

Left: This series of galaxy pictures was made using the HST in 1992. These objects are so remote that their light left them when the universe was two-thirds its present age.
Below: Every dot on this map of part of the sky is a distant galaxy. Far from being evenly distributed throughout the sky, they are grouped into clusters, superclusters, and lines, with some areas relatively devoid of galaxies. Black rectangles are poorly observed areas.

There is a solution to this problem if most of the helium was made in the Big Bang.

Theory tells us that a few minutes after the Big Bang, the universe consisted almost entirely of hydrogen nuclei (single protons) and helium nuclei, in a ratio by mass of 70-75 per cent hydrogen to 30-25 per cent helium. The fact that hydrogen and helium exist today in just these proportions in the observable universe strongly supports the theory.

Using the Hubble Space Telescope in 1990, scientists observed the spectral signature of helium in the light of the quasar UM675. This object is 12 billion light years away, and its light began its journey to us at an early stage in the universe. The observations therefore suggest that the helium was produced in the Big Bang, rather than comparatively recently in stars.

The cosmological distance scale

All the methods of distance measurement rely on knowing the true brightness or size of a standard object, assuming that all similar objects throughout the universe have the same properties. For comparatively close galaxies, these standard objects are either the sizes of clouds of hydrogen gas where stars are forming, or the brightnesses of Cepheid variable stars, which are easily recognized. At greater distances, astronomers use the brightnesses of Type Ia supernovae for distance measurement. These exploding stars should always reach the same peak of brightness. Type Ia supernovae can be seen 1000 times farther than Cepheid variables.

In 1992, using the Hubble Space Telescope, astronomers observed Cepheid variables in the faint spiral galaxy IC 4182, 16 million light years

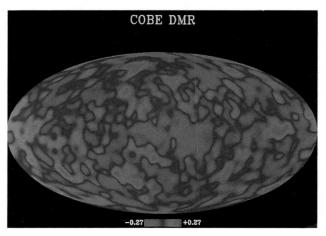

COBE DMR

Above: Variations in the cosmic microwave background of only 0.01 per cent are shown on this map made by the COBE spacecraft. Most of the variations are caused by instrumental noise but the slight effect remaining reveals lumpiness in the early universe.

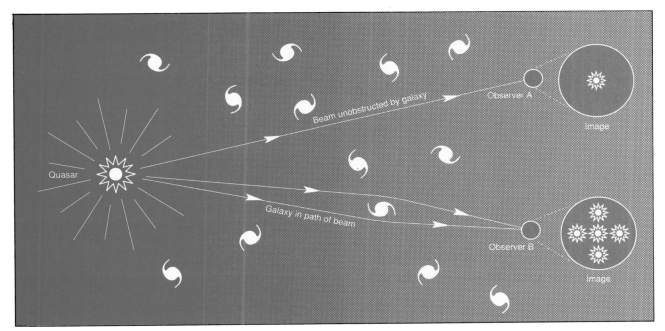

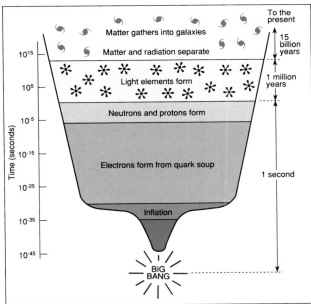

Above: Gravitational lensing occurs when light from a distant quasar passes close by a galaxy. In position A, unobstructed, the observer sees a single image. In position B, beams are bent by the galaxy, yielding a distorted image.
Left: History of the universe. After a rapid early inflation, the universe expanded uniformly. Within a few million years the first galaxies appeared.

This is thought to be a relic of the primeval explosion. About 300,000 years after the Big Bang, when matter and radiation in the fireball had cooled to a few thousand degrees, space became transparent and the visible and infrared radiation spread out through it. The universe has since expanded a thousandfold, and the original radiation has been diluted, redshifted, and cooled to a temperature of just 2.736 K.

Although it is evident that the universe was once hot and dense, the nature of the background radiation brought problems of its own. Cosmologists puzzled over how it could be so uniform across the sky, when it comes from widely separated parts of the universe which have never been in contact with each other. One solution is that the early universe expanded very rapidly, so rapidly that it has been called "inflationary".

Detailed surveys of faint, distant galaxies have led to the construction of computer-generated maps showing the locations of millions of galaxies. These maps show that galaxies are clustered, and that these clusters and superclusters are organized into strands of galaxies stretching across space for hundreds of millions of light years. They also reveal enormous voids, regions of space with almost no

away. A type Ia supernova occurred in this galaxy in 1937. The observations enabled a tying together of the Cepheid and Type Ia supernova cosmological distance "ladders". They indicated a value for the Hubble constant of about 45 km/s/Mpc, implying that the universe is between 14 and 20 billion years old. This is somewhat greater than the ages of the oldest stars, but contradicts work involving the same galaxy which favors a higher value for the Hubble constant of about 80 km/s/Mpc, which indicates that the universe is younger.

A vital piece of evidence for the Big Bang is the weak background of cosmic microwave radiation.

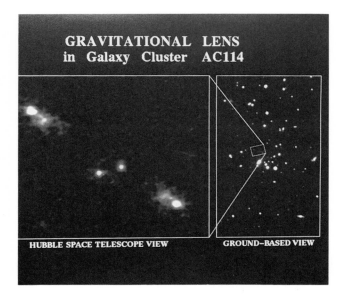

GRAVITATIONAL LENS
in Galaxy Cluster AC114

HUBBLE SPACE TELESCOPE VIEW — GROUND-BASED VIEW

Left: Evidence for dark matter in the universe comes from images of distant active galaxies which appear split in two by gravitational lenses. This 1992 Hubble Space Telescope view shows a pair of mirror images of a single distant object, at top left and bottom right, split by a much nearer concentration of matter, of which two parts can be seen at center. The number of such paired images helps determine the amount of dark matter.

galaxies, between the clusters. One of the greatest unsolved problems of cosmology is the origin of the galaxy clusters, superclusters, and voids.

To give rise to this large scale structure of the modern universe, some initial irregularities must have been imprinted. The "seeds" of the superclusters and great sheets of galaxies, hundreds of millions of light years across, would have disturbed the uniformity of the background radiation. In April 1992, excited scientists announced that the Cosmic Background Explorer satellite (COBE) had discovered temperature variations of just one part in 100,000 in the cosmic microwave background. Cosmologists are now trying to understand how these early "ripples" evolved into the galaxy clusters and large-scale structures we see today.

Dark matter

There is abundant evidence that there is a large amount of hidden mass or dark matter in the universe, quite possibly one hundred times as much as the visible mass. The amount of dark matter is crucial to answering the question of whether the universe is "open" or "closed". If it is open, then the universe will expand forever. If it is closed, the universe will eventually collapse back on itself, ending in a Big Crunch as the matter comes together. It has been suggested that the universe might oscillate between Big Bang and Big Crunch and could go on for ever. If the universe is neither open nor closed it is said to be "flat".

If the actual mean density of all matter in the universe is greater than a critical value, equivalent to about three hydrogen atoms per cubic meter, averaged over the whole of space, then the universe will eventually recontract. A value equal to the critical density marks the boundary between the open and closed universes. There is

some theoretical prejudice in favor of a universe where the average density of matter is very nearly equal to the critical value, and perhaps 99 per cent of the mass in the universe is hidden.

Cosmologists have been thinking about what form this dark matter might take. Suggestions have included old dead stars, very low mass stars called brown dwarfs, rocky bodies the size of planets or asteroids, black holes, or exotic particles. These hardly ever interact with ordinary matter, and have consequently never been observed. One dark matter candidate is the mysterious particle called the neutrino. This is a form of hot dark matter – called hot because the neutrinos would have been rushing around at high speeds, relative to ordinary matter, when the universe was young. Slower-moving particles are called cold dark matter. They have exotic names such as axions, photinos, gravitinos, and WIMPS (Weakly-Interacting Massive Particles). None of these forms of cold dark matter has yet been detected.

Gravitational lenses

Another new development is the successful use by astronomers of natural "gravitational lenses" to study the faint light from remote galaxies and quasars that would otherwise have been beyond the reach of even the most powerful telescopes. If a faint, distant galaxy or quasar lies behind a nearer cluster of galaxies then, if the cluster is sufficiently massive, light rays from the distant object will be bent by the strong gravitational pull of the cluster. The overall effect is that the cluster of galaxies acts something like a familiar glass lens would, magnifying and distorting the image of the faint galaxy or quasar behind it, producing arcs or multiple images. Gravitational lenses are being used to investigate star formation in distant galaxies, the mass of galaxy clusters, the existence of dark matter, the size and structure of distant quasars, and the scale of the universe.

The best evidence favors an inflationary, Big Bang model for the universe with a Hubble constant of between 40 and 80 km/sec/Mpc. Its overall geometry is very close to the simplest possible flat, Euclidean model. This means that the universe will just continue to expand for ever. If true, this is one of the most surprising coincidences in science.

Crystallography

Investigation of the basic internal structure of crystalline materials became possible only when X-rays were discovered a century ago. The regular spacings between atoms and molecules in a crystal are similar to X-ray wavelengths, so X-rays are diffracted by crystals. Diffraction is a bending of the rays around solid obstacles, which in this case are the actual atoms of the solid.

The regular arrangement of atoms in a crystal scatters a beam of X-rays into a distinctive pattern. Rather than picking up an image of the atoms directly, therefore, crystallographers have to measure the scattering pattern – the directions and intensities of the diffracted X-ray beams – and carry out the image construction mathematically. Structures found in this way are of interest to a wide variety of scientists in chemistry, physics, METALLURGY, mineralogy, GEOLOGY, biology, and other subjects.

Improved methods

X-ray crystallography has become much faster and more reliable in recent years. One important development has been the introduction of large sources of extremely high intensity X-rays, called synchrotrons, in which beams of electrons are made to travel in circles up to hundreds of meters across. They give out X-rays and other radiation. The high intensity – which can be millions of times greater than from conventional laboratory apparatus – makes it possible to study tiny crystals and very large molecules.

There have also been advances in new types of detectors. Instead of measuring X-ray intensity in just one direction at a time, the new instruments can cover an area of perhaps one square ft (0.1 m square) at a time, which speeds up measuring a complete diffraction pattern.

Measurements are increasingly being made from crystals cooled below room temperature, sometimes almost to absolute zero (-273° C). This drastically reduces atomic vibrations, so the structures obtained are more precise. Cooling also reduces any instability of the sample and allows samples which are not solids at normal temperatures to be studied.

Recent results

It is now usually a matter of routine to discover the structure of "small molecules" with up to about 200 atoms. This takes no more than a few days or even hours. The results give a detailed picture of the structure, with precise geometry such as the lengths of bonds and the degree of folding of rings. The technique is suitable for molecules of any kind, and it is used for important chemical substances such as pharmaceutical drugs, synthetic reagents and intermediates, and the products of research in synthesis. Often this is the only reliable way to find out just what makes up a new compound. Examples include anti-cancer agents, organometal-

Above: Computer graphics now show in three dimensions molecule structures found from crystallography. This is a typical small molecule, a nickel complex, with the nickel atoms shown red.
Right: This X-ray diffractometer is used for powdered samples, which are placed on the central disk. X-rays from the gray box are scattered by the sample and are picked up by the detector on the end of the arm on the right. Both arms can be moved around the sample.

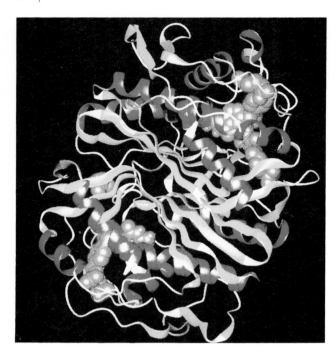

Above: A protein drug complex, modeled by computer. Instead of showing atoms, the main amino acid backbone is depicted as a ribbon, interacting with the orange drug molecules.

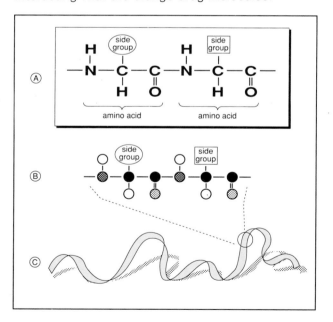

Above: Three ways of picturing a small part of a chemical structure. Amino acid groups consist of hydrogen, nitrogen, carbon, and oxygen atoms linked, with more complex side groups (A). These can be shown as simple atoms (B), but in graphics programs the amino acid chain is shown as a ribbon-like backbone which is then folded (C).

lic reagents in organic and inorganic chemical synthesis, and buckminsterfullerene (C_{60}) and many of its derivatives. In the case of C_{60}, low-temperature measurements have been particularly important, as the molecule is almost spherical; at room temperature it rotates freely in the solid, so individual atoms cannot be clearly distinguished.

Crystallographers are now able to study larger molecules such as proteins and viruses, which can often give excellent crystals, although many experiments may be needed to find the right crystallization conditions. Indeed, obtaining suitable crystals can often be the longest stage of the whole experiment. These large biological materials often include much water in their crystal structures, in a less well-ordered arrangement than in other crystals, and this reduces the intensities of the diffracted X-rays. Synchrotron radiation, area detectors, and crystal cooling are all important to make sure that the crystal does not decompose. Recent results include the first indications of the arrangement of molybdenum, iron, and sulfur atoms in the active center of nitrogenase, the enzyme responsible for the ability of some plants to use atmospheric nitrogen, and the structures of the viruses causing the common cold and polio in humans and foot-and-mouth disease in animals.

Not all crystalline materials are molecular; important work has been done recently on the structures of materials with extended arrays of atoms and ions. Crystallography has been essential in understanding the nature of high-temperature superconductors and of zeolites and other catalysts.

• FACT FILE •

- Crystallography is playing its part in the fight against AIDS. In 1990, teams of scientists at Columbia University and Harvard discovered part of the structure of a receptor molecule on T-lymphocytes in blood. These are the targets of the HIV virus (see IMMUNOLOGY).

- It is this structure into which the HIV virus fits itself. "We now know what the virus is seeing," said crystallographer Wayne Hendrickson of Columbia University. Significantly, the structure differed from what had been expected.

- Armed with a knowledge of the molecule's structure, it may in future be possible to construct another harmless molecule which will fit into it precisely, preventing the HIV virus from entering cells.

Dentistry

Today's children and young adults have far fewer filled or missing teeth than their parents. This is because in the 1940s and 50s it was discovered that people living in some areas developed far less tooth decay than those in other areas; the difference was due to traces of fluoride in the water. Since then many states have added fluoride to the water supply, with dramatic effects on the dental health of the population. Despite public concern about the possible dangers of fluoride, it is harmless in the doses used. The dramatic decrease in tooth decay has changed dentistry from the old-fashioned drill-and-fill methods to some exceptionally high technology.

The holy grail for dental researchers is a vaccine that will prevent tooth decay and gum disease. Despite a serious research effort, nothing has been produced yet but the next few years offer hope. Meanwhile, dentists have made huge progress in other forms of prevention and treatment.

Laser drills
A further cause of fear concern is that the mercury used in amalgam fillings may cause chronic poisoning; many dentists are replacing such fillings at huge expense to patients. However, research has shown that dental amalgam does not release mercury into the body; and that dentists, who handle a great deal of amalgam and would be the first to be poisoned, suffer no harm. Mercury remains one of the best filling materials as it is malleable when first mixed, lasts for many years, and does not crack under the forces of biting, chewing, and extremes of temperature in food.

The dentist's drill may soon be a thing of the past, replaced by lasers. By 1992 some 21,000 dentists worldwide had acquired hand-held lasers to vaporize tooth and gum disease. The pain of exposed teeth is caused by tiny tubules in the den-

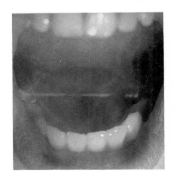

Right: The red beam of a high-powered helium-neon laser, along with an invisible high-power carbon dioxide laser, work on the root of a molar. The enamel is drilled conventionally before the lasers are introduced.

tine, the outer layer of the root. Lasing the exposed surface closes these tubules; one course of laser treatment works for up to three years. Lasers can also be directed into the pockets between teeth and exposed gum, killing the bacteria and allowing the gum to cement itself to the tooth again. The CO_2 laser, which uses carbon dioxide, is effective at removing soft tissues, and allows large areas to be treated at one sitting. The Nd:YAG laser, named for the rare earth element neodymium which is its active medium, has proved effective in clinical trials for removing decay, and for treating periodontal pockets.

Tooth replacement
Since 1980 it has become increasingly common for teeth that have been knocked out to be replaced. The tooth should be placed in milk, which will protect the delicate cells that stick it to the gum, and taken with the patient to the dentist. If no dentist is available, in emergency people can replace the tooth themselves, temporarily, using firm but not excessive pressure.

A new technique of tooth implantation was developed in Norway by Per-Ingvar Branemark in 1986. It has since become a commercial success; by 1990 there were 36 companies worldwide competing to produce the titanium parts. Called osseointegration, a biologically compatible implant is used that eventually becomes fused to the bone struc-

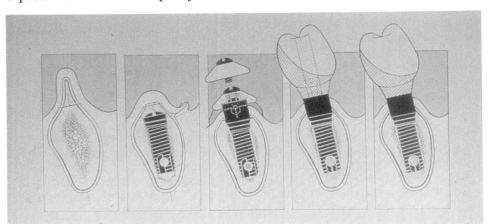

Left: A diagram showing the process of osseointegration, in which a titanium device is installed in the root. This is then built up with other titanium parts before a replacement tooth is added.

forming a pocket under the gum where bacteria may lurk. Originally, an operation called gingivectomy was commonly performed to remove this unattached gum, but it is being superseded by plastic surgery, in which tissue is transplanted from the roof of the mouth to a place where the gums have receded.

Newer techniques try to regenerate the periodontum, the delicate layer of cells that glue the tooth to the gum, and also to the bone itself. One involves transplanting fresh bone and marrow tissues, taken from the patient, around the teeth to form a new attachment apparatus. Another takes freeze-dried bone, which has fewer antigens than fresh bone from genetically similar donors. Barrier membranes are placed over the wounds around the teeth because they selectively allow certain types of cells to enter the wound area.

Left: The techniques involved in gum reconstruction. After the gums are peeled back and the tooth thoroughly cleaned, a biologically compatible material (shown in white) is inserted next to the root. This keeps away gum tissue which is biologically incapable of attaching to the tooth (shown in purple), while tissue which is capable of attaching to the tooth (shown in pink) grows upwards in the direction of the arrow. If the incorrect material grows next to the tooth, the gum will not attach properly and will provide gaps in which food can be trapped.

ture underlying the gum. The implants need frequent follow-up visits and scrupulous homecare.

Dental decay is caused by bacteria which feed on sugar in the mouth, producing lactic acid and plaque; the presence of sugar also allows the bacteria to multiply rapidly. The plaque provides a housing for the bacteria, and calcium in the saliva allows it to "fossilize". Although the importance of cleaning teeth after eating sweets has been known for decades, recent research has shown that cleaning teeth *before* eating sweets also protects the teeth, as there are far fewer bacteria to multiply.

A new technique for preventing decay is the use of sealants. Even before a child has any signs of decay, a soft plastic is applied to the tooth surface to fill in the pits and cracks where food and bacteria can accumulate. The plastic is then hardened with ultraviolet light or a chemical.

Gum disease

Older people lose more teeth from gum disease, properly called periodontal disease, than from decay. It starts with inflammation of the gums, then the bone and gums recede, exposing the root, which is highly sensitive to temperature and sugar. Gums also become detached from the teeth,

• FACT FILE •

- Modern dentistry is currently turning to high-tech tools such as computer imaging systems, surgical lasers, fiber optics, and CAD-CAM systems. A company based in Sacramento, California, Professional Services Institute, offers an imaging system that dentists can use to preview the cosmetic result of dental work such as orthodontic treatment (straightening) or tooth capping.

- Another computer imaging system – Pre-View Dental Imaging System from McGhan InstruMed Corp, Carpintaria, California – is modified from a French system used by plastic surgeons. These methods mean that the dentist does not have to make a physical model of the reconstructive work that he or she proposes, and can communicate with the laboratory by electronic mail or by mailing a floppy disk.

Electrical engineering

Electrical engineering, the practical application of electrical science, closely interacts with other disciplines, such as mechanical, hydraulic, and aeronautical engineering. But nowadays these fields are so closely linked that it is hard to draw the boundaries between them. The scale of electrical engineering systems covers an enormous range — from the microchips that form the key elements of computers, where distances are measured in microns, to the power systems that span a whole continent.

One mainstay of electrical engineering is the electric motor. In its most basic form this has remained the same for well over a century. The coils or windings of the motor are fed with electricity one after the other by means of a commutator - a set of contacts which spin with the motor. These regularly wear down, which is a major cause of motor failure. One recent development which overcomes this problem has been the integration of electronic switching devices and controls with electrical machines.

In commutatorless motors, for example, the currents are switched into the windings sequentially with electronic switches, rather than with mechanical ones. The new devices are more reliable than their electromechanical equivalents and can operate over a greater range of speed and load.

An unconventional type of motor, the switched reluctance motor, has a simple shaped iron rotor and several stationary windings. The current is switched into the windings sequentially, so that a rotating magnetic field is set up that drags the rotor around. Reluctance motors were used in a primitive battery-powered electric locomotive built by Robert Davidson of Aberdeen, Scotland in 1842, but they were too inefficient for general use. Recent work at Leeds University in England has shown that the inefficiency was not an inherent feature of the design, but was caused by the losses that occurred when the mechanical commutator switched the current on and off in the windings.

Electronic switching eliminates the losses and a simple, compact, easily controlled motor is the result. After 140 years in the wilderness the motor is making a comeback. Applications include washing machine drives, in which they can provide a very flexible washing cycle, high-speed machine tools, and light and controllable traction motors.

The switched reluctance motor, an unconventional magnetically driven motor which – after being abandoned in the 19th century – has made a comeback as a result of new technology. Left: An electric current is fed into each of the copper coils (right), creating a powerful magnetic field which is continually moving, driving the rotor (left). Above: The motor's simple design (left) makes it more compact than the conventional motor (right).

Left: General Electric's advanced superconducting electric generator. The generator's rotor, pictured here, was cooled to -452° F (-271° C) during extensive tests in which it produced over 20,000 kilovolt-amperes of electricity – more than twice what a conventional generator of the same size would produce.

When wound into coils that are well insulated and cooled with liquid helium, they make very high-strength magnets. With careful design, magnetic field strengths which are four to 10 times those of a conventional electromagnet can be achieved. Superconducting electromagnets find application in whole-body NMR (nuclear magnetic resonance) scanners for hospitals and in high-flux magnets for fusion experiments. General Electric has tested a prototype 20-megawatt electric generator with a rotating superconducting field winding. The generator is half the size of an equivalent conventional machine, yet more efficient.

The only superconductors known until recently became superconducting at temperatures only a few degrees above absolute zero, -459° F (-273° C). But a number of exotic compounds have now been found to have superconducting properties at much higher temperatures. For example, a ceramic based on calcium, lead, and copper oxides starts to superconduct at a temperature of -294° F (-181° C). It was developed after more than 15,000 different materials had been tested over a two year period, using robot equipment.

One day it may be possible to develop useful room temperature superconductors that can be wound into coils and are unaffected by mechanical stress and vibration. In the meantime, only "traditional" low temperature superconductors are being used in power applications.

Microscopic motors

A new Japanese development with potentially wide application is that of microscopically small motors. Toshiba announced in 1992 that it had made an electromagnetic motor less than $\frac{1}{10}$ in. (0.8 mm) in diameter. Although smaller motors have been made, they use electrostatic forces and have very much less power.

The wire in the coils of the new motor is only $\frac{1}{750}$ in (0.03 mm) thick. The device that wound the coils was adapted from one used to make the coils in the recording heads of video recorders. Weighing only $\frac{1}{10}$ oz (4 mg), which is about the same as a scrap of paper $\frac{1}{4}$ in (6 mm) square, the motor runs off a 1.7 volt supply.

Such a tiny motor could be used in surgical tools to be used inside the human body, such as a scourer for cleaning athersclerotic plaque from the inside of clogged arteries. It could also find a use in industrial plant which uses very fine tubes. One problem is that the motor runs at up to 10,000 rpm, and at slower speeds has very little torque, just like a car engine in top gear. To make it usable, a miniature transmission will be needed.

Superconducting devices

Another area of development in electrical engineering is the use of superconductors to reduce losses and raise efficiency. Superconductors are materials, such as niobium–titanium, that lose all electrical resistance at very low temperatures.

Trains in flight

Another application of superconducting magnets is in levitated transportation, where a magnet moving close to a conducting surface induces eddy currents, which in turn produce an opposing magnetic field, thereby generating lift. The vehicles literally float a short distance above the ground, thus virtually eliminating friction and reducing the energy needed to move the vehicle.

But a disadvantage of superconducting coils is that, unlike conventional motors, they produce a substantial stray field because there is no iron circuit to contain the field. Passengers are therefore likely to be subject to far higher levels of magnetic fields than in any other form of transportation. Any personal possessions which contain iron – keys, watches, tape recorders, and so on – would certainly be strongly affected by the magnetic field. Electric currents would be induced in a con-

Above: The Yamato-1 – a Japanese prototype boat which is powered by magnetizing water which passes through pipes on its hull. An opposite charge is then used to force the water backwards out of the pipes, propelling the boat forwards.

ducting object of any size – a metal tray, for example – whenever it was moved. This would not be dangerous but would mean that the person handling the object would find it resisting movement in disconcerting ways.

The German Transrapid high-speed transportation system avoids stray magnetic fields by using arrays of conventional electromagnets. They are attracted upward toward twin steel guide rails and provide lateral guidance. Speeds of 240 mph (400 km/h) have been achieved on the Emden test track in Germany. Transrapid links are proposed for Europe and for the U.S. – for example, from Los Angeles to Las Vegas. These should be operational in the late 1990s. The advantages of the Transrapid system are that it is much lighter and quieter than a high-speed train running on steel wheels and consumes significantly less energy per passenger mile.

The heavy part of the drive motor forms part of the track, so very little energy has to be transmitted to the vehicles – about 1.5 kW per ton lifted. Because the amounts of energy needed on board the vehicle are small, so-called transformer coupling can be used between the track and the vehicle, involving no physical contact. This avoids the need for mechanical current collectors in contact with a power rail or overhead cable. The vehicle can climb steeper gradients than a train, so there is less need for tunnels and cuttings.

Ships have traditionally been the province of steam and oil power, although electrically powered vessels are in regular use on reservoirs where the potential pollution from an oil-powered engine has to be avoided at all costs. Nevertheless, the first electromagnetically propelled paddle-boat was built by the Russian M. H. Jacobi and sailed on the River Neva during 1837 and 1838. In 1992, however, the Ship and Ocean Foundation of Japan went one better and built an electromagnetically driven boat with no moving parts. Yamato-1 cost five billion yen, is 100 ft (30 m) long, weighs 180

Above: In the switched reluctance motor, an electronic unit monitors the current flow and rotor position to control the power supply to the coils.

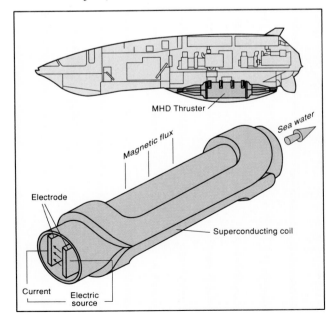

Above: Yamato's propulsion units have no moving parts but use electric and magnetic fields to create a flow of sea water.

tons and carries seven passengers. So far it has been cruising round Kobe Harbor near Osaka at a modest six knots. It is the precursor of much bigger boats that will be able to cruise at 100 knots.

The principle of operation is simple. Sea water can flow freely through two tubes running along the length of the boat below the waterline. Surrounding each tube is a superconducting magnet that produces a magnetic field at right angles to the flow of water. Electric current is passed through the water at right angles to both the flow and the magnetic field. A force is exerted on the water that propels it backwards through the tube and out through the nozzles, giving forward thrust. The advantages claimed for this *magneto-hydrodynamic* motor are the smoothness of the water flow and the absence of turbulence.

Electricity and efficiency

The introduction of processes using electricity can make significant savings in primary energy use. This has been demonstrated in the U.S., which now uses only seven per cent more energy than it did in 1973, even though the gross national product has increased by 43 per cent. A good example of the benefits of the introduction of a new energy-efficient electrical process is the concentration of dairy products to make dried milk – an important raw material in the food industry. The old process evaporated water using oil or gas. A new freeze-drying process uses electrically driven vapor compression to freeze water out, and consumes half the energy of the old process. When the technology is fully developed, it is hoped that the energy consumption will be down to one-sixth.

An electric arc is now being used to destroy toxic chemicals such as dioxins and polychlorinated biphenyls, which are not easily destroyed by conventional methods of incineration. Nufarm, the largest manufacturer of herbicides in Australia has commissioned equipment that uses an electric arc to break up noxious chemicals into their constituent atoms. These are recombined under carefully controlled chemical and physical conditions to form carbon dioxide, water, and hydrochloric acid, which are relatively harmless. The arc, which is struck between two copper electrodes in an argon atmosphere, creates a plasma that reaches a temperature between 18,000 and 27,000° F (10,000-15,000° C), which is twice as hot as the surface of the Sun. Waste can now be destroyed as it is produced, rather than having to be stored until it can be disposed of, with all the attendant risks of leakage and damage to the environment.

Another development with a potential environmental impact is that of the hybrid-drive vehicle, which has been used in an environmental concept car developed by Volvo since the late 1980s. The car overcomes the problems usually associated with electric cars – low power and short range – by using an onboard diesel-powered electricity generation unit. The car can be run on electricity alone in order to achieve zero exhaust emission on short runs, while on longer runs the diesel turbine can be used to recharge the power plant as the car is moving, thus giving a longer range while keeping exhaust emissions much lower than those of a conventional internal combustion engine.

Left: The control panel of a prototype Volvo Environmental Concept Car. The car overcomes problems normally associated with electric cars by having an onboard, diesel-powered electricity generator. The car's electric motor can be run entirely from the battery, so there are no exhaust emissions. The motor can also be powered from the diesel generator, or from a combination of the two methods. The three buttons at the base of the console are used to switch between these options.

Electronic engineering

No branch of science or technology has contributed so much to the development of the modern world as electronic engineering. From World War II onwards, advances in electronic engineering have been among the strongest influences stimulating progress in fields as diverse as astronomy, administration, automation, computing, health care, television, communications, transportation, weapons technology... the list is practically endless. Electronics has rightly been termed the most pervasive technology of modern times.

Reflecting this, the electronics industry now rivals in importance such established economic leaders as the automobile and oil industries. By the year 2000 it will have left even these behind to become the largest single industry in the world, with annual sales of electronic equipment exceeding $2 trillion.

Within this huge industry, electronic engineering tends to be divided into individual specialist sectors. Some of these, such as COMPUTING and TELECOMMUNICATIONS, are large enough to count as technological disciplines in their own right. Within them electronic engineers work on every kind of product from traditional mainframe computers and telephone networks to the latest personal computers and mobile phones. Other major electronics sectors include:

• consumer electronics: consumer products including TVs, stereos, calculators, VCRs, camcorders, and game consoles.

• medical electronics: health care products including X-ray and other diagnostic equipment, intensive-care patient management systems, body and brain scanners, pacemakers, body implants, and artificial limbs.

• industrial electronics: process control, factory automation, numerically controlled machine tools, and even robots.

• defense electronics and aviation electronics (avionics): radar, automatic pilots, inertial and satellite navigation, guided missiles, "smart" bombs, and all the "electronic battlefield" technology which was so effectively demonstrated in the 1991 Gulf War and the additional attacks in 1993.

Analog to digital

Although the electronics technology used in a personal stereo is not the same as that used in a cruise missile, there are common factors that unite all forms of electronic engineering, and trends that are bringing the different specialist sectors closer together. Perhaps the most important of these is the long-term trend, started in the 1960s and becoming almost complete in the 1990s, away from traditional analog electronics and towards digital systems.

Below: The quality control stage in the fabrication of silicon-based integrated circuit wafers, showing a close-up of a probe which automatically tests the circuitry of each chip on the wafer. Faulty chips are marked with ink from the two pens in the center.
Right: Technicians performing quality control tests on dynamic RAM (DRAM) chips. DRAM chips use capacitors rather than transistors for data storage.

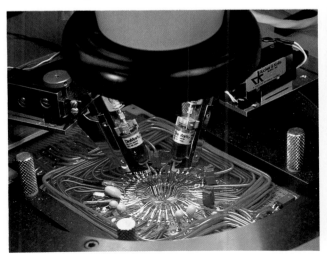

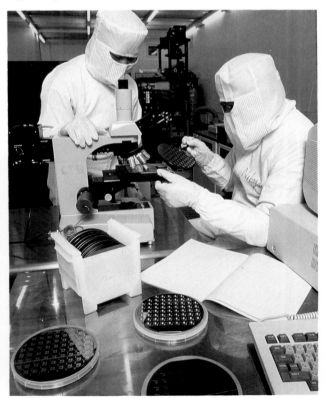

Left: An Iraqi target is pinpointed by an RAF electronic guidance system. Smart weapons help minimize civilian casualties.

The importance of this trend can be seen by looking at the consumer electronics equipment in the average home. For example, typical pre-1990s stereo systems often included both traditional analog cassette tape decks and all-digital Compact Disc (CD) players. In these systems, the cassette tape deck, based on the all-analog Compact Cassette (CC) approach to sound recording which dates back to the 1960s, will be built from up-to-date electronic components very similar to those used in the CD player. Yet the CD player, which is based on the all-digital approach to sound recording developed in the 1980s, offers much higher sound quality.

The two approaches typify the whole difference between analog and digital electronics. In the analog CC system, the electronic circuits have to handle sound in the form of varying voltages, with the voltage level in the circuit at any one instant being an exact replica or analog of the sound level at that same instant. As a result, any imperfection in the circuit which distorts the voltage level, however slightly, will distort the sound that the system produces. Even the most advanced electronic components introduce some distortion, so the analog CC system always produces some noise and "hiss".

By contrast, in the digital CD system the electronic circuits handle sound in the form of binary digits or bits, effectively just numbers. With this approach, the sound level at any one instant is represented not by a voltage level but by a numeric value stored in electronic form. As a result, even though the electronic components may distort the voltage levels quite severely, the numeric value of the sound level remains unchanged and the sound output undistorted.

This digital approach is now being extended to cassette recording. Since late 1992, stereo buyers have been able to add new-generation Digital Compact Cassette (DCC) decks to their systems. These new products use cassettes that are almost

Left and inset: A Digital Compact Cassette (DCC) player, designed as the successor to the compact cassette system. DCC cassettes (inset, compared with a standard cassette) offer greater durability with CD quality, and can both record and replay.

Left: With the advent of high-definition TV systems, come wide-screen pictures and digital stereo sound. Right: Interactive compact discs (known as CDI) offer a complete home-entertainment system including games and educational titles. Below: Automotive electronics provide not only a telephone link but also traffic and navigational information.

exactly the same as those used with the older CC models, and indeed can replay existing CC cassettes as required. However, by exploiting the digital approach they can offer CD-quality sound from lower-cost tapes, creating a huge new market for replacing the 1600 million CC decks in use worldwide. Also – by allowing stereo users to record as well as replay CD-quality sound – they join the new re-recordable "mini disc" CD systems in bringing a whole new dimension to home audio systems.

This same trend towards digital electronics in the home can also be seen in the latest developments in TV technology. Already some 10 per cent of the 100 million TV sets sold worldwide each year contain advanced digital electronics, but the actual TV transmissions themselves remain strictly analog. Moving to all-digital TV transmission would provide many benefits including much higher picture quality, from the 525 TV "lines" of the existing NATSC standard to the 1050 lines of the experimental new high-definition TV (HDTV) standards. As well as much clearer pictures, HDTV will also offer "widescreen" displays, extending the almost square pictures of existing TV screens to rectangular Cinemascope pictures to provide a true "movie-theater" look to TV programs. Stereo CD-quality sound will also be provided as part of the standard digital-TV package.

Already, the U.S. Federal Communications Commission (FCC) is committed to introducing new all-digital Advanced TV (ATV) services in the U.S. from 1995. This is likely to be the TV standard of the future, covering not just TVs but also new ATV VCRs, camcorders, and other video equipment. With market forecasts indicating that all these products will be taken up rapidly and enthusiastically by home viewers, the digital approach to electronics engineering is clearly set to take over the whole consumer electronics sector during the 1990s.

In doing so, consumer electronics will only be following the trend already established in other sectors of the electronics industry. Computer electronics has been all-digital almost from the start. Telecommunications has been becoming progressively more digital from the 1970s on, with the result that the nation's telephone networks will become practically all-digital during the 1990s. Even the much newer mobile phone networks, based on 1980s-vintage analog AMPS technology, are now being replaced by newer all-digital D-AMPS versions.

Progress in digitalization is also bringing once separate sectors of the electronics industry much closer together. Already, computing and communications have more or less merged into a single sector based on their common digital technology: increasingly, today's computers are designed to function solely within communications-based computer networks, while all-digital communications networks function entirely through the use of computer-based equipment. Electronic engineers talk of the 'convergence' of computing and communications as one of the key factors shaping the development of the industry. The important point

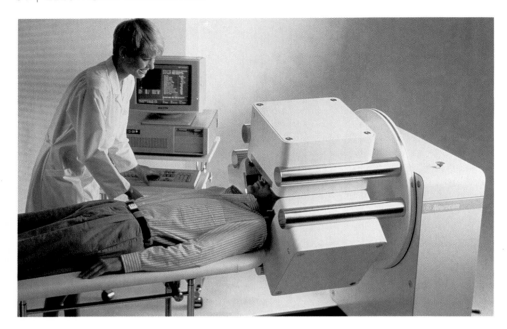

Left: A brain scan in progress. Medical electronics is a major sector of the industry, and patients now expect electronic monitoring.

is that convergence does not stop there.

For example, the move towards all-digital TV and video systems is now beginning to cause the convergence of the merged computer/communications sectors with the formerly quite separate consumer electronics sector. Already computers are being extended to work with video images, as well as with sound and data recordings based on the computerized version of the CD, the CD-ROM. Similarly, modern TVs are equipped with teletext and videotext data displays and even with printers. As the 1990s develop, the differences between a personal computer connected to the telephone network and an all-digital TV connected to a cable TV network will become insignificant. The result will be a new combination, a 'multimedia' terminal offering all the capabilities of a computer and a TV, and more.

Some idea of what this latest convergence of electronics sectors has to offer can be gleaned from the new interactive-TV or I-TV cable services launched in several U.S. cities in mid 1992. These provide the viewer with a keyboard that signals back over the cable TV network to allow the viewer to interact with the computers operating the TV system. For example, while watching a TV advertisement, the viewer can immediately place a credit card order for the advertised product, or, while watching a financial news program, request an on-screen "overlay" display of selected stock prices from a personal portfolio. More adventurously, TV viewers will be able to join in with live games shows and even participate in political debates.

As such interactive and multimedia TV services develop, the all-pervading power of digital electronics will come to play an even greater role in everyday life. At the same time, digital electronics will go on stimulating progress in industry, culture, medicine, defense, and practically every field of human endeavor.

Automotive electronics

Before the growth of digital technology, the electronic content of most automobiles was limited to the car radio. Now there is increasing use of digital electronics, making automotive electronics a thriving new sector with annual sales of over $10 billion worldwide.

In many car engines, electronics already control the tuning and ignition systems. In future, they will also be involved in "clean burn" antipollution exhaust systems, electronic transmissions, "drive by wire" electronic steering, and "active suspension" systems.

Among the navigation and instrumentation aids available will be trip computers, dashboard "moving map" navigation displays, radar displays and cruise control, radio-location using satellites, traffic-information systems, electronic-display "glass" dashboards, "head up" instrumentation displays, automatic fault location, and "black box" data recorders.

In the field of safety and security, as well as anti-lock braking there will be radar-assisted anti-collision control, drunk-driving prevention, electronically controlled 'air bag' restraints, and hijack alarms.

By the end of the decade, over $1800 of the cost of manufacturing a standard model car will go to electronics – and cars will be easier to drive, more economical and environmentally friendly, and, above all, safer and more secure as a result.

Embryology

"In the past ten years there has been a revolution in our understanding of animal development that cannot fail to ultimately have a profound impact on human medicine," reported a leading article in the *Lancet*, one of the world's most prestigious medical journals, in September, 1992. These advances have resulted from a fusion of classic experimental embryology with modern MOLECULAR BIOLOGY and developmental GENETICS. Embryology is the study of the development of an animal from the egg onward, and is often taken to refer to human embryology. However, clues to early human development have arisen from a quite unexpected source.

The breakthrough started with research on the classic experiment animal of genetics, the fruit fly, *Drosophila*. In the late 1970s, researchers realized that mutations of genes controlling early development would probably be lethal, and therefore conventional research, which has always looked at adult animals, would have missed them. They then screened fruit flies for the genes that, when they mutated, would give rise to dead larvae with recognizable abnormalities, such as missing segments, or conversion of one type of segment into another.

Most of these genes have now been cloned and scientists know what part of the body they are expressed in – that is, the part they control the design of – and at what stage of development. The result of all this effort has been a virtual gene-by-gene account of how *Drosophila* develops from a single-celled egg to a complex larva with many differentiated tissues and body parts.

Surprisingly, higher animals, including vertebrates, mammals, and even humans, contain genes which have considerable parallels with the fruit fly.

When the embryonic expression of many vertebrate genes were studied, they were very similar to fruit fly genes in the way they controlled development. Thus the *Drosophila* work has enabled scientists to identify genes in vertebrates that would have been difficult or impossible to find directly. Also, because we know that the important genes of early development are virtually the same in all vertebrates – whether fish, mice, or humans – we know that animal research has broad general applications to human beings.

Research findings have shown that many of the predictions made by theoretical biologists over the last few decades have been correct. First, there is an important class of genes – homeotic or selector genes – which codes for parts of the body rather than for separate tissues or cells. Such a gene

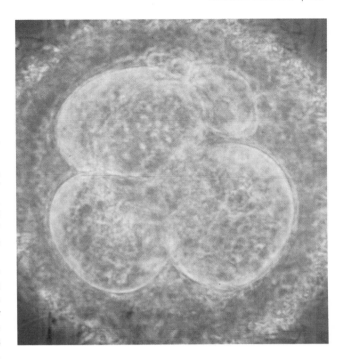

Above: Light micrograph of a primitive human embryo, composed of four cells following the initial mitotic divisions which ultimately transform a single-cell organism into one composed of millions of cells. This will ultimately be implanted in the uterine wall. The site of implantation determines the subsequent position of the placenta.

might be expressed in the front half of the body but not in the rear half. These homeotic genes code for transcription factors, whose function is to regulate the expression of other genes; they lie near the top of a hierarchy of gene regulation. Second, the body plan is specified by concentrations within each cell of chemicals that act as inducing factors or morphogens. In *Drosophila* these are the same as growth factors. The crucial element is the concentration gradient – that is, the way the concentration increases over a short distance. Third, the stability of gene expression depends, often and perhaps always, on positive feedback, whereby a gene is kept active by the product it makes.

The fruit fly research has shown that the mechanisms of embryonic development are based on some simple rules. Every egg is slightly asymmetrical, regardless of species, so there is always a gradient that can trigger the formation of a gradient of morphogens.

The gradient leads to activation of one or several of the homeotic genes in different parts of the embryo; the exact concentration of the gradient determines which genes will be activated. These gene products turn on other genes that produce further sources and targets for further morphogen

Left: Embryology research using fruit flies of the species *Drosophila*. The flies are bred in the bottles, then the number of mutants from each pair of parents is counted.

gradients, which activate other combinations of homeotic genes.

Each small, multicellular region of the embryo soon becomes uniquely specified by the activation of a combination of homeotic genes. Once established, these codings are maintained by positive feedback and the gradients are no longer needed. Later on in development, each combination of morphogens will trigger the genes involved in the eventual differentiation of particular organs and tissues.

The techniques of GENETIC ENGINEERING have opened up a whole new field of experimentation. In 1991, two scientists at the University of Utah in Salt Lake City, Osamu Chisaka and Mario R Capecci, inserted a mutant homeobox gene called Hox-1.5 into mice embryos. Homeobox genes contain codes for the operation of other genes. Mice which were born with the resulting mutations had no thymus, an organ necessary for regulating the immune system.

The mice, which all died within 12 hours, also had abnormal parathyroid gland function and defective hearts and arteries – characteristics of a life-threatening human birth defect called DiGeorge syndrome. Although the defective gene in mice is on a different chromosome from the one implicated in about a fifth of people with DiGeorge syndrome, Chisaka and Capecci still believe that Hox-1.5 might play a role in the human disorder.

They speculate that several genes working in concert, including Hox-1.5, may cause the syndrome, or that the gene may trigger the disorder by activating an adjoining gene on the chromosome. They plan to determine whether embryonic cells which are destined to form part of the nervous system *and* interact with homeobox genes cause defects directly, or if these cells must migrate elsewhere in the embryo in order to cause damage.

Embryonic development research promises insights into the workings of the human body. Eventually we may have a clue to understanding the degenerative diseases of old age such as osteoarthrosis, cancer, heart disease, cataract blindness, and deafness. And we may have taken the first important step in developing treatments that can attack conditions such as cancer at their root causes.

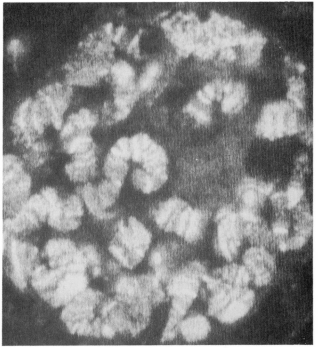

Left: Salivary gland chromosomes from the larva of the fruit fly are widely used in research into genetics and developmental biology.

Endocrinology

The science of endocrinology, which deals with the understanding and treatment of hormonal and metabolic illnesses, has undergone rapid change in the 1980s and 90s.

Diabetes, a condition caused by insufficient insulin production, affects approximately 12 million Americans, many of whom eventually suffer from eye problems and kidney failure. This was once thought to be due to poor control of blood sugar, but research in the 1990s shows this is not the case, and other causes must be sought. However, new research has shown that when diabetics receive kidney transplants, the new kidney lasts better if the patients subsequently has a pancreas transplant. The mechanism for this effect is unknown, and the transplanted pancreas does not prevent the progression of eye troubles.

Acromegaly, a far less common disease than diabetes, is caused by excessive growth hormone, which enlarges the bones of the face, hands, and feet. Growth hormone is produced in the brain under the influence of two substances, a releasing hormone, and *somatostasin*, which inhibits its production. A new compound, *octreotide*, has been developed that mimics somatostasin, lowering blood levels of growth hormone in 75 per cent of acromegaly patients and relieving their symptoms. It has to be injected, though doctors are trying to

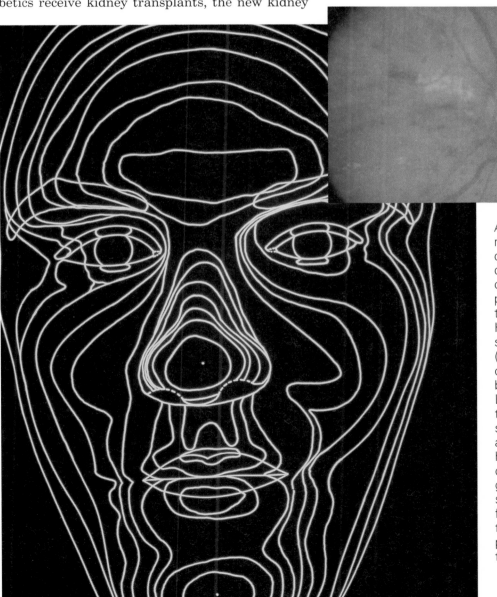

Above: Diabetic retinopathy – an eye disease caused by diabetes – is the most common cause of preventable blindness in the Western world. Hemorrhages (dark red spots) and exudates (pale orange areas) caused by diabetes can be seen on this retina. Left: A contour map of the face of a person suffering from acromegaly – enlarged hands, feet, and face caused by excess growth hormone. Jaw size measurements from the map are used to check that the patient is responding to treatment.

develop a continuous infusion pump worn round the body, similar to that used by many diabetics. Octreotide seems more effective than the present standard therapy, *bromocryptine*, though some patients respond better to bromocryptine or a combination of both. Octreotide is more expensive than bromocryptine and more difficult to administer, so its use is restricted to those who do not respond to bromocryptine, surgery, or radiotherapy on the pituitary gland, where growth hormone is made.

There have been major advances in reproductive endocrinology, including the recognition and analysis of *inhibin*, a hormone whose existence was postulated before it was actually discovered. Inhibin is made by the granulosa cells of the ovaries and the Sertoli cells of the testicles, and is under the control of follicle-stimulating hormone (FSH) produced by the pituitary. Inhibin may lead to a method of screening for early ovarian cancer as blood levels of inhibin may prove to be a test for granulosa-cell tumors of the ovary.

Another hormone, *activin*, is also produced in nonhormonal tissue including bone marrow, where it enhances the maturation of developing red blood cells and increases the circulating concentrations of red blood cells and hemoglobin. Inhibin has the opposite effect in bone marrow, inhibiting red cell production. The next few years promise to see many more valuable discoveries of this fascinating group of hormones, which have proven very useful in treating a wide range of hormone imbalances and tumors.

Hormone replacement therapy (HRT) is now becoming a widely accepted method of avoiding some problems of old age in women (see GERONTOLOGY). The medication may be taken orally or as a patch applied to the skin.

Parathyroid hormone, produced in tiny glands embedded in the thyroid and controlling calcium levels in blood, has been known for years. Now it has been discovered that there is another hormone which increases blood calcium, but with important differences. It has long puzzled scientists that many cancer patients have high blood levels of calcium even though they do not have secondary tumors in bone, a common cause of this. The calcium is now known to be due to parathyroid-hormonelike protein, called PLP for short. Results just emerging show that PLP is present in 50 per cent of patients with breast cancer and 33 per cent of those with multiple myeloma.

Finally, there is promise of a male contraceptive pill, though it could be used as a pill for men and women alike. *Gonadrotropin-releasing-hormone* (GnRH) was discovered in the 1970s. Produced in the brain, it acts on the pituitary, making it produce the gonadrotropins that stimulate the ovaries

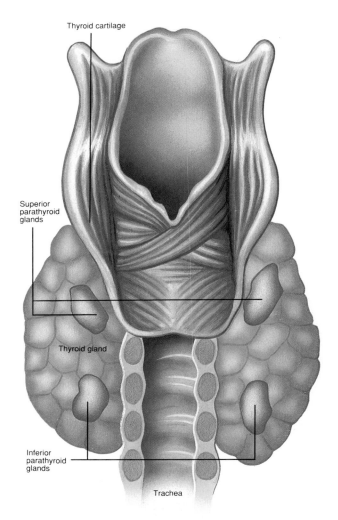

Above: Diagram showing the location and structure of the thyroid and parathyroid glands. The parathyroid gland controls calcium levels in the blood, but recent research has found another very similar hormone which has been linked to cancer.

and testes. By making GnRH inhibitor drugs, scientists have been able to greatly reduce sperm production in men. However, the men treated with these drugs also lose libido so they also need replacement testosterone therapy. Combined injections of anti-GnRH (daily) and of testosterone (one injection every two months) have been shown to reduce the sperm count to nil by 10 weeks while maintaining normal sexual function. Sperm production resumes after the end of a course of injections. The method is to be tested as part of a seven-country trial by the World Health Organization of potential male contraceptives. Whether this form of contraception will be widely accepted remains to be seen.

Energy production

Energy planners are faced with two problems of growing urgency: how to ensure an adequate supply of energy for the foreseeable future and how to curb the damage to the environment from burning fossil fuels. Fossil fuels are by far the most important source of energy. About 40 per cent of the world's primary energy needs are met by oil, 27 per cent by coal, 21 per cent by natural gas, 6 per cent by hydroelectricity, and 6 per cent by nuclear electricity. But the Earth's supplies of fossil fuels are being consumed 100,000 times faster than they are being formed. And with new concerns about atmospheric pollution and global warming, the search is on to find alternative, sustainable, and clean sources of energy.

Energy on the road

Of the world's production of oil, about half is burned up in road vehicles. With about 500 million vehicles on the roads and the number rising rapidly, we cannot expect an early move away from fossil fuels for road transportation. But in some areas, especially the large urban areas, emissions of carbon monoxide, nitrogen oxides, and hydrocarbons are reaching worrying proportions. And the average tankful of gasoline releases up to 400 lb (180 kg) of carbon dioxide to play its part in the global greenhouse effect.

Automobile manufacturers are researching methods of making cleaner and fuel-efficient engines, but in the longer term more drastic solutions will be required. California has taken a lead by legislating that one in 50 of new cars sold in the state from 1998 will have to produce no air pollution at all. This is a severe condition and only one technology could feasibly meet the deadline – the electric car.

So far electric traction has found application in only a few low-powered and specialized vehicles such as golf carts and delivery vehicles. Although the attractions are obvious – no immediate pollution, low noise, efficient use of energy – the chief obstacle to the widespread use of electric vehicles is the cumbersome lead-acid battery. A practical electric car would need lead-acid batteries weighing up to 1000 pounds (450 kg) to give a range of a mere 100 miles (160 km).

Fortunately the Californian deadline has spurred manufacturers to research new types of battery. Two systems under development may be ready for the market by 1998. The sodium-sulfur battery is the more promising. It contains electrodes of sulfur and molten sodium enclosed in a ceramic casing. With a weight-for-weight capacity three times that of a lead-acid battery, it could run a car for an acceptable 150-200 miles (240-320 km) between recharges. However, with an operating temperature of around 660° F (350° C) it poses problems of corrosion and safety.

The other possibility is a nickel metal hydrid battery but this is not yet sufficiently developed. Despite these developments, even the most promising new technologies cannot compete with gasoline for energy storage per pound and it will still require several hours to charge a battery.

Engineers are also looking at ways to make electric cars more efficient so that they waste less energy. New lightweight electric motors with electronic control could deliver 100 horsepower (75 kW) and weigh only 100 lb (45 kg).

Of course, the electricity has to come from somewhere, and for the near future power stations will continue to depend heavily on fossil fuels.

Left: Mexico City is one of the smog capitals of the world. Dependence on gasoline as an energy source for transport is responsible for a huge production of carbon dioxide. Though other fuels are technically feasible, the huge infrastructure surrounding the use of gasoline-fueled cars will make it hard to introduce any alternative.

However, economies of scale ensure that the pollution emitted by the central generation of electricity to run cars would be considerably less than that emitted from the gasoline-powered vehicles they replace. And the immediate benefit is that the emissions are removed from the places where they do the most harm – the congested centers of our ever-growing cities.

Power from the Sun

Of all the alternative sources of energy, solar power is among the most attractive. It is clean, plentiful, and free for the taking. Sunlight arriving at the Earth carries about 15,000 times the world's energy needs.

There are several ways to use solar energy. The simplest and oldest is conversion to heat as in the rooftop solar panels sometimes used to supplement domestic water heating systems. A more sophisticated approach is to collect solar energy over a wide area and concentrate it on to a boiler to raise steam which can then drive a conventional turbine and generate electricity. Thermal solar plants in Daggett, California together produce about 400 megawatts – equivalent to a full-size nuclear installation.

But the most promising lines of research are in photovoltaic devices, the "solar cells" that are used to power space satellites and pocket calculators. Based on silicon wafers, PVs convert radiant energy directly to electrical energy with efficiencies of 12-16 per cent. New types of cell, which reach efficiencies of more than 30 per cent, are under development. PVs can be used as roof and wall cladding to heat buildings in the winter and run air conditioning in the summer. Germany is the leader in applying PV technology, and has unveiled plans for the world's biggest PV solar power plant. It will be built in the state of Thuringia and will generate 4 megawatts.

Approximately 50 megawatts of PV solar plant is installed around the world every year to the value of $700 million and the market is rising rapidly. The bulk of U.S. solar energy equipment is sold to the developing world where the absence of electricity distribution grids makes solar energy particularly attractive. Small installations can drive telecommunications equipment, water pumps, and refrigerators.

Storage, always a problem with electricity generation, is particularly acute for solar electricity since production is determined by the weather rather than demand. A radical solution is to use solar electricity to electrolyze water into its constituent gases of hydrogen and oxygen. The hydrogen could then be stored, transported, and used as a clean-burning fuel, the only emission being water vapor. Some planners foresee a full-scale

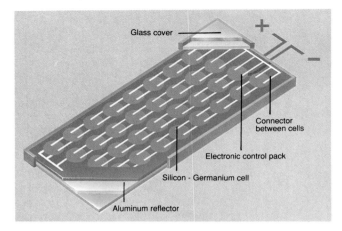

Above: Solar panels consist of a number of individual photovoltaic cells joined together. Each cell produces only a low voltage but by making suitable connections the output can be chosen for each application. The low efficiency of solar cells means that large numbers, covering a huge area, are needed to produce significant power.

Above: This solar array at Barstow, California, consists of 1818 mirrors each 23 ft (7 m) square. These are computer controlled to focus the Sun's rays on to the central tower, where the heat generated turns water into steam at 900° F (500° C). This in turn drives a turbine generating 10 MW of power for eight hours a day.

"hydrogen economy" where new and safe methods of storing hydrogen will allow it to be used as the prime fuel for industry and transportation. Experimental hydrogen-burning cars are already running, though many practical questions remain to be solved.

THE ITER DEVICE

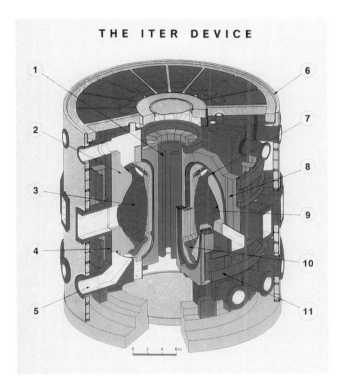

Left: Cutaway view of the ITER device. The central solenoid (1) generates a large current – 25 million amps – which heats the gas inside the tokamak to some 200 million K. The shield/blanket (2) converts the fast neutrons produced by fusion reactions within the plasma (3) into heat at a few hundred degrees which can then be used to drive a generator. The plasma is contained within a vacuum vessel (4), and exhaust products are extracted through the plasma exhaust (5). A cryostat (6) uses liquid helium to keep the vessel at just a few degrees above absolute zero, enabling superconducting coils (7, 8, and 11) to produce the magnetic field needed to contain the plasma. The first wall (9) has to contain the immense heat within the plasma, while the diverter plates (10) direct the spent helium "ash" away through the plasma exhaust.

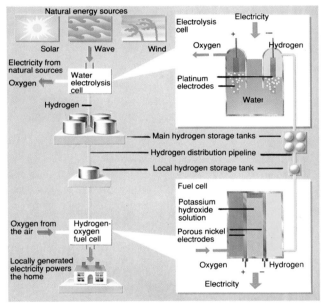

The promise of fusion

In the longer term, far into the next century, problems of energy supply and pollution may be eased by nuclear fusion. There are two ways to release the energy of the atomic nucleus: fission and fusion. In fission, energy is released by breaking up large nuclei such as uranium or plutonium. This is the principle underlying the nuclear power industry, but it has its attendant problem of nuclear waste transportation and storage.

Fusion energy is released by forcing small nuclei together rather than by splitting large nuclei apart. It is the source that powers the Sun and the hydrogen bomb. In both cases hydrogen nuclei are fused to create helium. Fusion can release much more energy than fission, and is cleaner with less danger of pollution.

Physicists and engineers around the world are working together to find ways of controlling nuclear fusion. Four teams are now working on experimental fusion reactors – in the U.S., the European Community, Japan, and the former Soviet Union. Now all four have agreed to cooperate on the next stage, the construction of an International Thermonuclear Experimental Reactor – ITER.

Three international design teams – based in San Diego, Munich, and Japan – are being assembled to tackle the formidable problems of devising and building a 1000 megawatt reactor. If ITER goes ahead on schedule it should be completed by 2005 at a cost of $7.5 billion.

The fuel used will be deuterium and tritium,

Above: In theory, the Earth is not short of energy: the problem is that it is usually needed in different places and times from those where it is available, either as solar, wave, or wind power. Hydrogen could perhaps provide a solution to this problem. It is easily made by passing an electric current through water – the process of electrolysis – and could be stored and piped where it is needed. It can then be used in a fuel cell, which recombines the hydrogen with oxygen from the air to generate electricity. The main drawback to the use of hydrogen is its flammability.

heavy forms of hydrogen. Ample deuterium is found in water and tritium can be made from naturally occurring deposits of lithium metal. Extremely high temperatures are required first to ionize the gases and then to impart sufficient

Right: Nuclear fusion is considered to be the most likely new source of energy in the next century. This view is of the inside of the tokamak in an experimental fusion system, the Joint European Torus, at Culham, Oxfordshire, UK.

kinetic energy to the nuclei to overcome their electrostatic repulsion and collide, allowing the strong nuclear forces to take over and fuse them. In the Sun, the reactions proceed at a stately 15 million K, but ITER will maintain temperatures of approximately 200 million K.

No material container can possibly withstand such temperatures. The ionized gas (or plasma) will be confined in a doughnut-shaped magnetic field in a device called a tokamak. The vessel will be about 52 ft (16 m) in diameter and contain a magnetic field, 200,000 times as strong as that of the Earth, generated by 16 giant superconducting magnets, each cooled to 4.5 degrees above absolute zero.

ITER will be intrinsically safe. Unlike fission reactors, the amount of fuel inside ITER at any one time is so tiny that there is no danger of a runaway reaction. The waste products will not be radioactive, but neutrons produced in the reaction will induce radioactivity in the structure of the machine. This is one problem engineers will need to address before fusion becomes a practical proposition.

ITER will operate for at least 15 years. It will not generate electricity, but will give physicists and engineers the know-how they need to build a fusion power station. It could be the middle of the 21st century before fusion energy plays a part in our everyday lives. Such is the scale of the undertaking that most of the scientists working on ITER today may never live to see the fruit of their labors.

Fusion in a test tube?

In March 1989 the scientific community was rocked by a startling announcement. Two respect-

ed chemists claimed to have harnessed nuclear fusion, not in a multi-billion dollar reactor like ITER but in a small glass jar in their laboratory in Utah. Martin Fleischmann and Stanley Pons reported that they had observed excess heat being generated in an electrolytic cell of palladium electrodes immersed in heavy water (deuterium). When they passed electricity through the cell, they said, the current drew deuterium ions from the water into the palladium electrodes, where they were fused to create helium.

In an intense flurry of activity around the world scientists scrambled to repeat the experiments. Some found excess heat, some did not. Some found neutrons from the reaction, some did not. Funding agencies launched research projects into what had been dubbed "cold fusion." The state of Utah provided $5 million towards a Cold Fusion Research Institute.

The debate became increasingly fraught and ill-mannered. Physicists accused the chemists of not understanding nuclear reactions and having poor experimental technique. Chemists accused physicists of not understanding the complexities of electrochemistry. In 1991 the Cold Fusion Research Institute was closed down. Most scientists now regard cold fusion as an anomaly.

In August 1992 Fleischmann appeared at a meeting of the British Association for the Advancement of Science and revealed that he and Pons were now working on cold fusion at a secret location in France with funding from the Japanese government. It seems we have not heard the last of one of the strangest episodes in modern science.

Environmental science

Environmental scientists may be experts in physics, biology, GEOLOGY, CLIMATOLOGY, or even MATHEMATICS, and their job is to investigate how human beings interact with the environment and how we affect it. By bringing together the threads of many different investigations, they give a global picture of what is happening to the Earth as a result not just of technological activity but also of natural activity.

Disaster predictions

The work of environmental scientists covers the air we breathe, the flow of water, and the soil we depend on for our crops. But it is the study of the atmosphere which has brought the work of environmental scientists into the news recently.

At the beginning of 1991 pundits were fearing a major environmental disaster – and they were proved correct, but not in the way they expected. The cause for their worries was the impending Gulf War. Their worst fears were realized when Iraqi action set hundreds of oil wells ablaze, their smoke turning day into night in Kuwait. The news media predicted that the fires would take years to extinguish, and that the resulting pall of smoke would affect huge areas of the globe.

The fires were put out within eight months. The smoke stayed close to the ground and crops beyond the Gulf region were not unduly affected. There were, however, serious side effects from the vast lakes of up to 150 million barrels of unburned oil that gushed from the uncapped wells. Efforts were

then diverted into bulldozing dikes to prevent the oil from spilling into the Gulf. Pumps were used to suck the oil up from the lakes, but this in turn led to problems of storage. Over a period of years, underground water supplies to the region could be irreversibly polluted by the oil. It takes only 2 pints (half a liter) of oil to pollute 250,000 gallons (a million liters) of drinking water.

Even the air could be polluted by the lakes of standing oil. Experts from the World Conservation Monitoring Centre feared that hydrocarbons evaporating from the oil could affect the health of people living in the area. Wildlife, too, suffered: birds trying to land on what appeared to be a lake of water became instantly coated with sludge.

However disastrous the Gulf War was for the region, it was another event which had the most pronounced effects on the globe and its atmosphere. On April 2, 1991, Mount Pinatubo, a vol-

Right: Ice-core data from the GRIP site in Greenland shows that 11,500 years ago there were periods of intense biomass burning and volcanic emissions – data which have implications for current research on global warming.

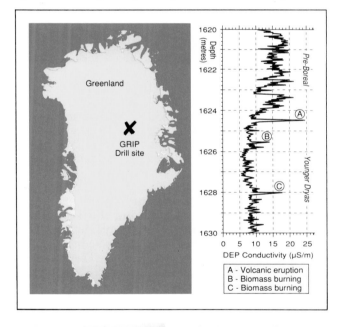

A - Volcanic eruption
B - Biomass burning
C - Biomass burning

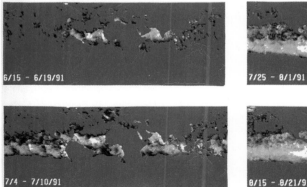

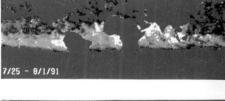

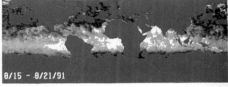

Left: A series of maps showing the increasing concentration of aerosol particles in the upper atmosphere after the eruption of Mt. Pinatubo in 1991. Aerosols began to occur over the tropics for the first time during the eruption. Each increase of 0.1 in the color scale represents a 1 per cent increase in solar radiation reaching earth.

there is no proof that either of these occurred as a result of the ozone hole, the link was made in many people's minds.

In the spring of 1992 there was international alarm as measurements made over northern Europe showed that an ozone hole was also opening up there. The eruption of Mount Pinatubo the year before had increased the number of particles in the upper atmosphere, which speeded up the ozone-killing reactions. It was feared that up to one per cent of the ozone layer could be depleted

Left: Oil fires raged in Kuwait after the Gulf War. The fires were extinguished within eight months using a Hungarian machine known as 'Big Wind' – a converted aircraft engine which literally blew out the flames. There was serious damage to the local environment, but the effects did not spread far beyond the Gulf as had initially been feared.
Right: The 1991 explosion of Mt. Pinatubo left the Philippines covered in ash and had a serious worldwide effect.
Below: A balloon launch in Sweden to study ozone levels and pollutants.

cano in the Philippines which had lain dormant for 600 years, began to erupt. On June 12 it exploded violently. While the immediate concern of the scientists studying the outburst was to prevent loss of life among the population, the event had repercussions which were still evident throughout the world a year later.

Pinatubo's worldwide effects

For a number of years, environmental scientists have warned of damage to the layer of ozone (a form of oxygen molecule) which lies some 15 miles (25 km) above the Earth's surface. This layer is vital to life on Earth as it screens the Sun's most harmful ultraviolet rays. Yet in the early 1980s, scientists in the Antarctic found that the ozone layer there was severely depleted – there was a hole in the ozone layer over the Antarctic. Looking for the cause, they pinpointed a reaction between the ozone and gases called CFCs – chlorofluorocarbons, used widely in such household items as refrigerators, fire extinguishers, and aerosol sprays. At low temperatures and under the influence of ultraviolet light, these broke down the ozone molecules.

The scientists reported their findings amid much skepticism. But when Australian doctors began reporting an increased incidence of melanoma, a form of skin cancer, which is the result of excessive skin exposure to ultraviolet, public concern was aroused. In Chile, also affected by the ozone hole, sheep which spent their lives in the open began to go blind from cataracts. While

each day – leading to a 25 per cent drop by the end of the northern hemisphere's spring. Regrettably, the ozone actually produced by industrial pollution occurs at the wrong level in the atmosphere and at the wrong time, to have any effect on the ozone hole.

Governments finally began to take action to force industry to replace CFCs by other materials which would not have the same effects. In February 1992, President Bush committed the U.S. to cease production of CFCs by the end of 1995 and shortly afterwards the European Community agreed likewise. But as CFCs take five years to reach the ozone layer, and persist for up to a century, environmental scientists are concerned that the extra effects of manufactured CFCs in addition to volcanic eruptions could have a major effect on world agriculture. Ultraviolet light can damage young crops, particularly in the spring when the ozone hole is at its worst.

Global warming
Ironically, the eruption of Mount Pinatubo promised to reduce the immediate effects of another potential environmental catastrophe – global warming. Environmental scientists have long been aware that the composition of the atmosphere is changing. The proportion of carbon dioxide in particular, but also of other gases which are lumped together as greenhouse gases, is increasing.

The name of this phenomenon comes from the tendency of these gases to block the flow of heat away from the Earth's surface. As long as the flow

Above: A symbol of global warming – crops will suffer dramatically as huge areas turn into desert.
Below: Scientists now realize that volcanic eruptions could tip the delicate balance of the world's climate.

outwards is in equilibrium with the inflow of solar warmth, the globe remains at an equitable temperature. But if the greenhouse gases interfere with this, the world will heat up, with drastic changes in the world's agriculture as some areas dry up, others become wetter and the viability of staple crops such as rice and wheat changes in their traditional growing areas. An increase in global temperature could also affect the sea level, as snow and ice currently on land masses melt, with clear consequences for the large populations that live close to sea level.

While many experts are convinced that global warming should be taken seriously, governments are not so easy to persuade that they should take drastic steps to curb industrial output of greenhouse gases, which are produced both naturally and by human activities. Carbon dioxide is released into the atmosphere by using natural gas, coal, and oil – "fossil fuels" – to generate electricity and fuel for road transportation. A further contribution comes from burning of forests in the Third World as people clear land to grow crops. At the Earth Summit in June 1992 many developing nations were hoping to force the U.S. – the world's biggest producer of greenhouse gases – to join them in agreeing to curb its own activities and maintain output of carbon dioxide at no more than 1990 levels by the year 2000.

Some people in the U.S., however, feel that this would involve a change in their lifestyle that they would not willingly accept. It would mean a greater use of public transportation and a reduction in the use of home heating and air conditioning, for example – even though the reasons for the change are not directly visible.

A few hot summers and water shortages in the U.S. during the 1980s – the hottest decade on record – persuaded many people of the reality of the greenhouse effect. The chance of a hot summer in Omaha almost doubled by the early 1990s, for example. But the eruption of Mount Pinatubo could change all that. The dust and sulfuric acid droplets from the volcano were predicted by NASA scientists to cool the globe by about 1° F (0.5° C), bringing milder weather to the U.S. corn belt but the return of severe winters to Moscow. By 1996, however, the prediction suggests the return of global warming.

Carbon tax

Environmental issues do not recognize international boundaries. But it is hard for individual governments to act, as the Dutch discovered when, in 1992, they planned to levy a "carbon tax". The tax, planned to be related to the amount of energy a fuel produces and the amount of carbon dioxide it generates, was based on one proposed by the European Community. It could have the effect of doubling the cost of fossil fuels.

There was an immediate reaction from large industries faced with crippling increases in their costs. Major firms threatened to move their operations away from Holland. The dispute threatened to topple the government, which also planned to bring in taxes on agricultural chemicals, water supplies from non-renewable underground sources, and the dumping of garbage. One task facing environmental scientists in future years is to devise an acceptable means of levying such taxes.

• FACT FILE •

- In the summer of 1992, work was completed in an effort to discover how the Earth's atmosphere has changed over a vast time span. In Greenland, an international team of scientists drilled their way through a mile and a half (2.5 km) of ice, down to solid bedrock, through layers deposited as snow up to half a million years ago.

- By extracting a core of ice as the hole was drilled, the scientists obtained a unique record of environmental conditions on Earth long before homo sapiens appeared. The acidity of the sample indicated the presence of particles from ancient volcanic eruptions.

- In the new core, scientists found evidence for the first time of "biomass burning" – that is, forest fires. These may have been caused by major volcanic eruptions or other natural events in the past. Like volcanic particles, the clouds of smoke from big fires could have a major effect on the global climate, reducing temperatures over a large part of the Earth's surface.

- Other measurements of isotopes in the ice core have revealed the varying temperatures of the polar regions over many thousands of years. For example, after the last Ice Age ended 10,700 years ago, the average temperature rose 13° F (7° C) within just 50 years, showing that rapid natural temperature changes can occur. Current global warming trends are about 1° F (0.5° C) per century. Such studies can help shed light on the complex links between atmospheric dust, carbon dioxide, and temperature.

Epidemiology

The science of epidemiology is not only the study of epidemics: it is the study of who gets diseases, and why. In its broad sense, it covers the whole of mathematical medicine. It also studies the efficacy of treatment, compares one treatment with another, allows health care providers to project future needs of populations, and measures the effectiveness of health treatments and health workers.

AIDS, which was first recognized in 1981, has been a challenge for epidemiologists, both for mapping where the disease started and how it spread, and for projecting its future incidence and the resources needed to tackle it (see MEDICINE).

U.S. virologist Dr. Robert Gallo discovered that HLTV – human T-cell leukemia virus – caused a rare type of leukemia found in parts of Japan that were settled by Portuguese traders, who had apparently brought it from Africa in the 15th century. A variant strain of this virus, which caused AIDS, also festered in Haiti, brought there by French-speaking black administrators who worked in Zaire after it became independent and had dispensed with its European administrators.

AIDS in Africa had not been recognized as immune-deficiency, but was simply called slim disease because patients became progressively thinner from diarrhea before slowly dying. The AIDS virus reached France from Zaire, and the U.S.A. from Haiti, and it took a while before the two strains were recognized as fundamentally the same. The French cases were in men and women alike, while the first U.S. and British cases were mainly in homosexual men and drug abusers. Since AIDS is transmitted by body fluids that enter via injection or trauma, it is spread by injections, sexual intercourse, and blood transfusions. Women are more at risk from heterosexual intercourse than men, as men deposit their body fluids in women, but not vice versa. In parts of Africa, more than 50 per cent of prostitutes have AIDS.

By making mathematical models of the speed and path of how the virus has spread, epidemiologists predict how many new cases might be expected yearly, and how to identify those most at risk and the advice to give them on avoiding infection.

A major tool in the testing of new drugs is the *double-blind* test. Randomized, double-blind clinical trials, particularly of drugs, have been common since the 1950s, and since the 1960s have been compulsory for new medicines. Double-blind means neither the patient nor the doctor knows what the patient is taking; only the pharmacist can find out which batch of pills is which. Trials compare an active substance with a *placebo* – an ineffective pill which appears identical to the one

Above: A technician at the Centers for Disease Control at Atlanta, Georgia, carries out an enzyme-linked immunosorbent assay (ELISA) on blood samples. In a double-blind trial, samples are identified only by a random number, so no one carrying out the test can influence the results either consciously or unwittingly.

under test – or with another active substance, usually the established treatment for the condition.

In Britain, a trial designed to test the efficacy of treating moderately high blood pressure showed that the active treatment was effective in 66 per cent of patients – but that the placebo was effective in 33 per cent. It also showed that treating mild hypertension with drugs was barely justified, as it saved very few lives but at great expense, and that side effects lowered the quality of life for many participants.

Since the 1980s epidemiologists have recognized that many double-blind trials may not be truly double-blind because the patient knows what he or she is getting. This may be because of their side effects or their physical properties ("When I threw them down the toilet, doctor, I knew they were different from the old pills because they floated."). In the early 1980s, some AIDS sufferers could only get the drug AZT by volunteering for a trial, and

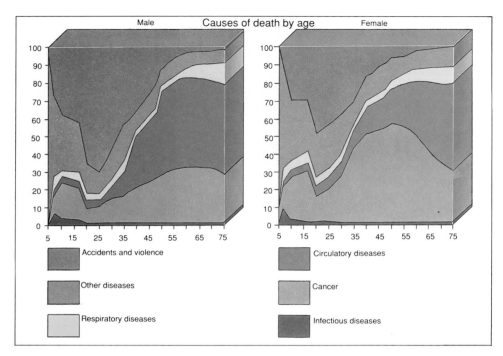

Causes of death by age

Male

Female

Accidents and violence

Other diseases

Respiratory diseases

Circulatory diseases

Cancer

Infectious diseases

Left: Causes of death for males and females in the U.K. in 1986, plotted by age. Changes in such graphs over time, and comparisons made between different countries, can help in locating causes of diseases and in studying the effectiveness of treatment.

many of them, understandably, took their tablets to a laboratory for analysis, thus breaking the code. A good double-blind trial should report that patients were asked to guess at the end of the trial what they had been taking, and what proportion guess correctly (50 per cent can be expected to guess correctly by chance).

Scientists also recognize that patients report side effects with placebos; if these side effects are unpleasant, the substance is called a *nocebo*. In the mid 1980s, food additives became associated with adverse effects in many people's minds; such effects, the opposite of placebo effects, are called nocebo effects.

In the 1990s epidemiologists started to strongly assert that if systematic reviews of treatment were regularly updated, reliable recommendations for treatment (for example, for early breast cancer) could have been made much sooner. They also pointed out that many clinical trials are wasted to some degree: either because they are not published or because they are ignored.

For example, a systematic review in 1980 of randomized controlled trials would have shown that a course of steroids given to women expected to give birth prematurely substantially reduces the risk of their babies being born ill or dead. Repeated failure to conduct such a review and apply the results has not only resulted in the unnecessary suffering of tens of thousands of babies, but also meant that neonatal care has been more expensive than it should have been.

Failure to publish many treatment trials, often because they show a treatment is ineffective, has led to "publication bias", so that many treatments have been perceived as being more effective than they really are, because only "positive results" were disseminated.

Right: Speed is vital in spotting and checking the spread of diseases. At Britain's Center for Disease Control, computers are used to log the results from over 25,000 clinical samples taken daily across the country and sent by phone. This network quickly reveals outbreaks of both infectious diseases and food poisoning which can often be traced to individual batches of food.

Forensic medicine

The discovery in 1985 in Brazil of a body said to be that of the Nazi Josef Mengele led to one of the most celebrated forensic investigations ever conducted. Mengele, known as the "Angel of Death", was the senior doctor at Auschwitz, the Nazi World War II concentration camp, where he assessed the suitability of Jewish prisoners for work or extermination. He also conducted "medical" experiments on inmates.

The investigation made use of a multitude of techniques devised to help forensic specialists discover the identity of bodies that have decomposed beyond recognition. In this case, the body had been buried since February 1979.

Few of the cases in which the help of a forensic expert is requested capture the public's interest like this one. The specialty of forensic medicine, broadly defined, covers any aspect of medicine which relates to the law. Clinical forensic work is concerned with living patients, from measuring the level of alcohol in the blood of those accused of drinking and driving, to the examination and taking of samples from rape victims. Those doctors who practice forensic pathology, by contrast, occupy themselves with dead bodies.

Related fields are forensic serology, the study of blood groups and other inherited elements of the blood in relation to crime and the law; forensic toxicology, which is the study of poisoning in relation to crime and the law; and forensic odontology, where dentists advise on problems such as identification of corpses (by correlating their teeth with dental records) or whether a suspect may have been responsible for a bite left on a murder victim.

In all these subspecialties, the scientific techniques that forensic experts use in their work come under the heading of forensic science.

Forensic pathology

Forensic pathology is the most famous branch of forensic medicine. The forensic pathologist will be called in to investigate deaths that are the result of accidents, that are associated with medical treatment, that are sudden or unexpected, or that are criminal or suspicious. It is the cases in the last category – people who may have been murdered – that often attract enormous publicity in the media.

At the scene of a murder, police will want the forensic pathologist to help them establish key

Above: A picture of Nazi "Angel of Death" Josef Mengele, found in his house in Brazil after his death. Mengele's decomposed body was identified using modern forensic pathology techniques.

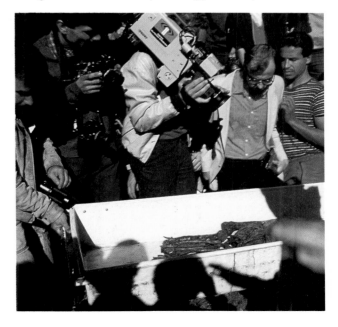

Right: Mengele's exhumed body, Sao Paulo, 1985. Comparisons with Mengele's dental records and tests on the skeletal remains confirmed with reasonable certainty that the remains were, in fact, those of Mengele.

facts such as the cause and time of death. If the body is badly decomposed, they may need help in identifying the body.

Numerous new methods are now helping forensic pathologists to provide more accurate answers to these questions. It may be possible to determine the cause of death simply by inspecting the scene of the murder or by carrying out an autopsy.

One new technique makes it possible to confirm that someone who apparently drowned was in fact still alive when he or she became submerged, ruling out the possibility that murder had been carried out by some other means and the body disposed of in water.

This method involves looking for diatoms, microscopic algae found in both salt and fresh water. If someone takes water into his or her lungs when drowning, diatoms can pass from there into the bloodstream and be carried in the circulation to organs such as the liver. Tests on the liver at autopsy can show that diatoms, which have walls impregnated with silica, are present. But diatoms will not enter the circulation if the person's heart has stopped beating before his or her body enters the water.

Diatoms can even provide clues to the place of death: different types are found in fresh and salt water, and even in different localities.

Time of death

Establishing the time of death has always been a problem for police and pathologists. Three factors may be of help: the drop in temperature of the body; the order of decomposition of the various organs; and the onset and passing away of rigor mortis. But such characteristics are of only limited use in estimating the time of death, and are of no use at all after three or four days have passed.

At this stage, the somewhat unlikely specialty of forensic entomology may be able to provide some clues as to the time and place of death. Particular species of flies will arrive on the body after it has cooled sufficiently for them to lay their eggs on it. These will hatch into maggots, whose age can be assessed. So if the maggots are five days old, then death must have occurred at least five days earlier – assuming the body was exposed soon after death. If the temperature outdoors is very cold, yet blowfly maggots are present on a body found outdoors, this suggests that death took place in an environment warm enough for flies to be active, probably indoors, and was then disposed of elsewhere.

As time elapses after death, the type of insects which feed or breed on the body changes. Blowflies, bluebottles, and greenbottles that are attracted early on are absent during the later stages of decomposition. Three to four months

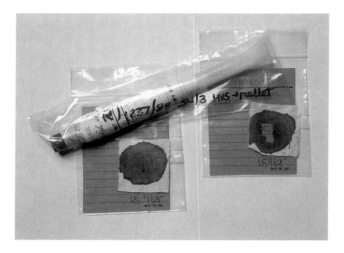

Above and below: Typical samples from which a DNA fingerprint can be obtained in order to identify a rapist. Above: Two pieces of bloodstained cloth and a vaginal swab from which a DNA fingerprint was obtained during the investigation of a rape case. Below: clockwise from top – pubic hair which has been trapped in a comb with cotton wool; blood and semen stains on various garments and a swab.

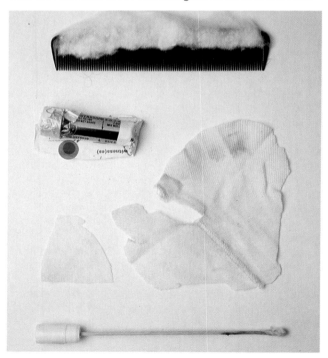

after death, the tiny maggots known as cheese skippers are commonly present.

The presence or absence of specific insects can also suggest where the death occurred, information that may be very useful if the body is discovered only after it has been moved. For example, infestation with the larvae of *Coelota frigida*, which breeds in seaweed which contains animal remains, indicates that the body has been at the seaside.

Methods to help identify the corpse have improved greatly in recent years. Study of the skeleton, provided it is complete, makes it possible to determine the person's sex and find out what height the person was. In young people, the extent to which the long bones have progressed in their gradual change from cartilage to calcified bone makes it possible to provide a good estimate of age.

Characteristic features of the teeth can give clues to age and race. Scanning electron micrographs of the teeth show that their surface becomes smoother as people age. People of Asian origin have distinctive pits on their teeth, visible under high magnification.

The patterns of the sinuses, which are visible on an X-ray of the skull, are unique to each individual. So if a radiograph of the skull already exists of the person thought to have died, comparison with a second X-ray taken after death should make it possible to confirm the tentative identification – or not.

It may also be possible to make the identification by superimposing an X-ray of the skull on to a photograph of the person thought to have died. If the photograph is of the same person, key "landmarks" on the face, such as eye sockets and the position of the chin, will match up with those on the X-ray.

Starting with the skull, artists have tried to make models of what people looked like when they were alive. They have used clay to build up the muscles of the face, according to the positions and sizes of the areas where the muscles were originally connected to the skull.

Computer portraits

Such techniques are now being superseded by computerized methods. Laser scanners can produce a very accurate series of measurements describing the dimensions of the skull. Fed into a computer, the measurements can be translated into a three-dimensional image of the skull, which can be rotated on the screen and viewed from any angle.

Although this work is still in its early stages, it is now possible to "flesh out" the image of the skull on the screen, using software that provides information on the average thickness of the skin and muscles at each point on the face. Researchers hope eventually to collect enough data about the

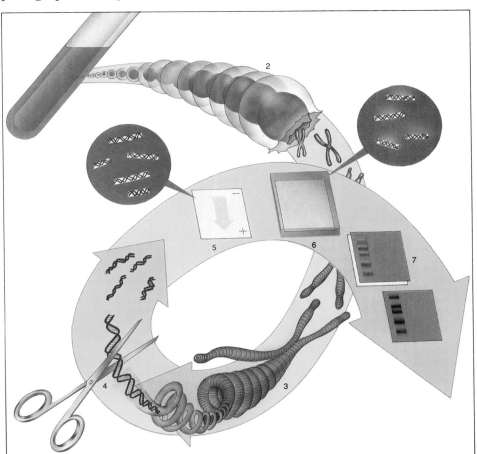

Left: The process of genetic fingerprinting: (1) A blood sample is taken. (2) The DNA is extracted. (3) Each strand of DNA is isolated. (4) The strands are chemically sliced into fragments. (5) The DNA is transferred onto a nylon sheet. (6) The radioactivity shows up and (7) is developed on an X-ray plate. Different plates for the suspects, the victim, and the evidence found at the scene of the crime are checked against each other to see if they match.

Above: A pathologist checks DNA samples for evidence of matching. The patterns on the plate are complex, and the analysis is often done manually.

average thickness of the facial tissues in people of various ages and races in order to produce accurate images of what the person to whom the skull belonged looked like when he or she was alive.

Many of these techniques, and others similar to them, were used to identify the body of Mengele. It is now generally accepted that after Mengele escaped from Europe following World War II, eventually settling in Brazil, he assumed the identity of another Nazi, Wolfgang Gerhard. He was buried in 1979 under Gerhard's name after he drowned, having suffered a stroke while swimming.

Two Europeans who lived in Brazil and said they had sheltered Mengele claimed that the body buried as Gerhard was in fact Mengele's. The investigation that followed was conducted by three teams of forensic experts from Brazil, West Germany, and the U.S.

They found that the height of the person to whom the skeleton had belonged was 174 centimeters, the height given in Mengele's SS records. The skull showed evidence of a gap between the two front teeth, which Mengele had. Fillings in the original teeth that remained in the skull corresponded with Mengele's dental records dating from World War II. Tests on his bones put the age of the person who had died at 69 – the age Mengele would have been in 1979.

One test, carried out by the West German forensic team, clinched the uncertainty for many of the scientists. They compared a video image of the skull with a video image of a photograph of Mengele when he was young. After adjusting the size of the two images, they were able exactly to superimpose the features of one onto the other.

On June 20, 1985, they decided that there was "reasonable scientific certainty" that the remains definitely had belonged to Mengele.

• FACT FILE •

- "Genetic fingerprinting" has revolutionized much forensic work. Developed by Professor Alec Jeffreys of Leicester University in the U.K., it makes it possible to identify an individual by examining his or her DNA.

- Genetic fingerprinting can be used to determine whether a blood stain found at the scene of a crime belongs to a suspect, whether a child is the offspring of its mother's husband or her lover, or whether a potential immigrant to a country really is related to his or her family which resides there.

- The method relies on the fact that there are highly variable regions within the DNA which consist of short sequences repeated many times. No two people (except identical twins) share the same set of these so-called hypervariable regions. A child shares about half of its hypervariables with its biological mother and the rest with its biological father. Jeffreys identified short sequences within these regions that were the same in many different people. This made it possible to develop a test for the regions which would demonstrate different individuals' patterns of them.

- The first step in the technique is to obtain DNA from the tissue being tested. Enzymes added to the DNA act like "chemical scissors", chopping the molecules into pieces of unequal size. Adding pieces of DNA that are radioactively labeled and which bind to the hypervariable regions of the DNA in the sample makes it possible to show the pattern of the regions in the sample being tested. The result is a unique pattern of stripes, which looks something like a supermarket bar code.

- The method can be used to test very old forensic samples. It can also be applied to tiny samples of material that have been amplified with the polymerase chain reaction (see GENETIC ENGINEERING). In a development in 1992, the race of a person can be deduced from a sample, thus narrowing the range of suspects.

Forestry

Less than one third of the world's land surface is covered in forests and woodland. But this proportion is changing. In temperate countries forest cutting and regeneration are more or less in balance; a few countries have even increased their forest cover this century through sustained tree planting. But in the tropics, about 4 million acres (17 million hectares) of forest are disappearing each year. Estimates of the global loss vary, but by comparing old and new infrared images taken with the Landsat satellite, scientists have found precise figures for some areas.

All uses of wood – for fuel, pulp, lumber, and panel products – total about 8,260 million board feet (3,500 million cubic meters) per year. The world is well able to supply this quantity of wood since it roughly equals annual new growth. It is local imbalances in wood demand and land clearance for other uses that cause deforestation.

Population increase is often made a scapegoat for deforestation, but the causes are mainly social and political. People clear forests to plant subsistence crops, then exhaust the nutrients in the soil and move on; governments sometimes encourage this by moving people into forest areas to save other land for cattle ranching or export crops that will bring in cash to pay foreign debt. The need for cash has also encouraged excessive logging.

Deforestation affects the livelihoods of forest dwellers and those living around forests who depend on them for food and fuel. In 1980 the United Nations Food and Agriculture Organization reported that 96 million people in Africa, Asia, and tropical America lacked enough wood to meet their heating and cooking needs. When wood is too scarce to use for boiling water, disease takes hold. Clearcutting – removing all trees at one time – speeds erosion, diminishing the productivity of the soil and silting downstream reservoirs.

Deforestation affects us all. Tropical forests are immensely rich ecosystems containing as many as 5 billion species of plants and animals, many of which are being forced into extinction before they can even be discovered. Less than 1 per cent of tropical forest plants have been tested for their medicinal value, yet that small number has produced drugs to treat such diseases as glaucoma, heart disease, and cancer. Perhaps most importantly, the destruction of forests increases the amount of carbon dioxide in the air, contributing to global warming.

Alarm over tropical deforestation and its consequences led to the International Timber Trade Agreement in 1984 and the formation of the Tropical Forest Action Program in 1985. Countries

Above: A California pine seedling nursery. Forested areas in temperate regions are increasing, according to a 1992 survey. As overproduction of cereals creates "grain mountains", more land is being set aside for forests. The area of New Hampshire under forest has increased from 50 per cent to 86 per cent in 25 years, and most European countries have also increased their tree cover. Some argue that the new forests are important absorbers of carbon dioxide.

attending the U.N. Conference on Environment and Development in June, 1992 in Rio de Janeiro agreed on a non-legally binding statement of principles for a global consensus on the management, conservation, and sustainable development of all types of forests.

Social and community forests

Forests are no longer just timber factories. Third World countries have launched social forestry programs such as those encouraging local peoples to create tree plantations to provide products such as fuel wood, poles, fodder, and even organic fertilizer in the form of nutrient-rich leaves. Forestry research can assist these projects; foresters in Costa Rica, for instance, have tested over 150 species of trees to see which are best suited to reforest former cattle pastures. Such tests have shown that native species of hardwoods, formerly thought unsuitable for plantations, will grow rapidly even without forest cover.

But research is useless unless the political and economic forces behind deforestation are dealt with. Many experts believe the best way to preserve forests is not to leave them alone but to manage them to produce medicines, fruits, nuts, and other products besides timber, making them

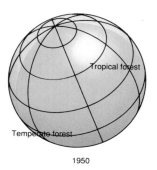

1950

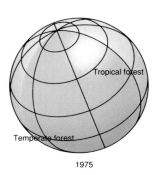

1975

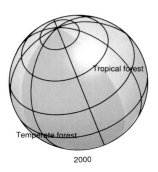

2000

Left: Deforestation is a major problem as the demand for land and wood increases. The globes show the loss of tropical forest (actual and predicted) in the 50 years between 1950 and 2000. The destruction of forests greatly increases the amount of carbon dioxide in the air.

• FACT FILE •

- The explosive force of the 1980 eruption of Mount St. Helens in Washington State leveled trees for miles around and laid a thick blanket of fiery ash over a vast area of approximately 160,000 acres. The land could recover on its own; it had done so after previous eruptions in the 1800s and countless other times throughout prehistory. But foresters saw an opportunity to make the whole area a laboratory to learn how to deal with similar disasters in the future.

- 110,000 acres were left untouched to study the natural restoration process. The other 50,000 acres were divided into test plots to compare various approaches to reforestation. Some trees were planted with fertilizer, some with upright cedar shingles to shade the seedlings, some with no assistance at all. Over six years, more than 25 million trees were planted.

- Scientists found the young trees grew faster than expected, probably because there were no tall trees to block sunlight and, at first, no animals to browse on the seedlings.

- At least 20 types of shrubs and 80 different herbs have returned on their own. Animals and birds that formerly inhabited the area also came back, helped by the U.S. Forest Service, which installed bird houses and drilled holes in fallen trees to provide habitats. Still, it will be many years before the reforested area returns to its former vigor and decades before the natural area recovers.

valuable enough to compete with other land uses. Using forest selectively, preserving some woodland cover at all times, and sensitively managing plantations to enhance edge effects and preserve stream and river margins and areas of natural woodlands all enhance biodiversity. Wood production from forests is sustainable; the priority today is to make sustainable these other values, as well.

Above: A Japanese technique, announced in 1992, which could revolutionize the timber industry uses a giant microwave oven to make logs pliable. They can then be compressed by a simple ram into a square shape. The method squeezes out moisture, thus improving the wood's hardness and quality. Crooked logs are straightened, and waste at the sawmill is reduced by up to 50 per cent. The squeezing process takes less than seven minutes.

Genetic engineering

In 1953 James Watson and Francis Crick, at the University of Cambridge, discovered the structure of the "molecule of life". This is deoxyribonucleic acid or *DNA*. They found it has a double-helix shape, with two long strands twined around each other, like two spiral staircases. Each DNA strand has a series of chemicals arranged in a coded sequence, like letters in a sentence of instructions.

In living cells the two DNA strands can separate and make copies of themselves. DNA's chemical sequences are organized in "units" known as genes, and they contain the instructions for building and running a living organism. During cell division DNA copies itself, passing from parent cell to daughter cells, and parent to offspring, carrying the genes that are the blueprint for life. The detailed structure of DNA and how it works is crucial to MOLECULAR BIOLOGY, while the nature of genes is explained by GENETICS.

During the past 40 years, molecular biology has brought about many advances in the understanding of DNA and other types of nucleic acids. Researchers can now manipulate lengths of DNA, and therefore genes, *in vitro* and *in vivo* – literally, in laboratory test tubes as well as in living cells.

Pure molecular biology is concerned with how genes function at the most detailed level. Genetic engineering is a relatively new science that could be described as its practical extension and application. Genetic engineering techniques have uses in farming, industry, medicine, and research. Useful products of genetic engineering include antibiotic drugs, enzymes (which control and speed up chemical reactions), crops with higher yields, and possibly farm animals that grow more efficiently.

Gene manipulation is not a new process. Since early civilization, people have manipulated genes by selecting and breeding certain animals or plants that had desirable combinations of genes. Modern technologies extend this approach to the molecular level. We no longer need to wait for animals or plants to breed. Researchers separate, analyze, move around, and recombine a host of genes from microbes, plants, and animals.

The basics of genetic engineering involve transferring genes to new places, new cells, even entirely different animals and plants. Here they can be used as blueprints for making products, and to

Below: The process of microinjection, which is used to introduce new DNA into the genetic makeup of a cell. The work is done through a light microscope and visualized on a video display unit as pictured here. The circular cell is stabilized by a suction tube (right) while the probe on the left introduces the genetic material. The dark area at the center of the cell is the nucleus.

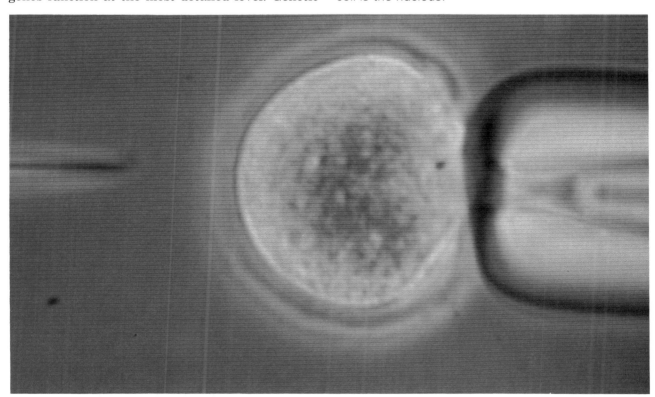

Left: Microinjection being used to introduce foreign genes to a cell during research on cancer-inducing genes. Genetic research of this sort led to the development of the anti-cancer drug interferon. A suction probe holds the cell still while a finer probe penetrates the nucleus and manipulates the genetic material.

enhance or change the workings of other genes, for our ultimate benefit.

Plasmid vectors

The task of isolating and analyzing genes makes use of "carriers" that transfer the genes from one situation to another. These carriers are known as *vectors*. Vectors used in genetic engineering are usually products of previous genetic manipulation. They provide ways of replicating (multiplying or copying) pieces of DNA and transferring them from one cell to another. Vectors in common laboratory use include *plasmids* and *viruses*.

Plasmids are small circular pieces of DNA that can exist independently in living cells. Plasmids have their own control genes – coded sequences of DNA that are necessary for their replication. They can also be engineered to carry genes with special features, such as making the cells that harbor them resistant to an antibiotic drug.

The ability of plasmids to multiply themselves and act as genetic "markers" when inside a cell, makes them attractive for research use. In order to get plasmids into living cells, especially the researcher's "workhorse microbe", the bacterium *Escherichia coli*, the cells are made *competent*. This means that their cell membranes are weakened so that they can take up the plasmids. The bacteria may then be grown on a nutrient agar (jelly) that contains an antibiotic drug. If the plasmids carried genes for resistance to the antibiotic,

then only those bacteria containing the plasmids will be able to grow and produce colonies on the jelly. In this way, bacteria that have not taken up the plasmids can be screened out.

Where possible, plasmid vectors are made with small sections of DNA that can be attacked by specific enzymes, the *restriction endonucleases*. The enzyme cuts or digests the plasmid at this site, to change its circle of DNA into a string of linear DNA. Then a similarly digested "target" piece of DNA is joined to the linear DNA by another enzyme, *DNA ligase*. The DNA ligase also joins the ends of this longer, linear DNA back into a circle. The result is a plasmid with the target gene incorporated, ready for further manipulation.

Some plasmids have so-called *polylinker sites*, where a wide range of DNA fragments can be accommodated.

Phage vectors

A virus is minimal life. It consists of a length of DNA or sometimes RNA, wrapped in a protein coat. The types of viruses known as *phages* are another type of gene vector. The term phage is a short for bacteriophage – a virus that infects bacteria. Many phage vectors are based on the type of phage known as lambda.

A phage's DNA can be manipulated in the same way as plasmids. It can take up larger segments of extra DNA compared to a plasmid. The DNA is packaged in its protein wrapping to make the com-

Above: A researcher studies a video image of DNA bands which have been sequenced by electrophoresis in an agar jelly (seen in background, blue). Once the different bands have been separated, they are stained using ethidium bromide. This fluoresces under ultraviolet light, highlighting the positions of the DNA bands which are viewed using a video camera.

plete phage; this is used to infect suitable host bacteria. Plaques resulting from phage infection of bacteria growing on agar jelly can be screened (see MICROBIOLOGY) to detect any DNA fragments which may be of interest.

Another class of vectors is the *cosmids*. These combine the versatility of plasmids with the larger DNA-carrying capacity of phages. All of these vectors can be used to obtain and make multiple copies of identical genes from living cells, a process called gene cloning.

Some plasmids and cosmids are known as shuttle vectors. They contain DNA codes for replication in relatively simple cells like bacteria, and also in the more complex cells of higher plants and animals. They therefore allow cloned genes to be transferred from lower to higher organisms, and vice versa. This "transfection" is a useful tool in studying diseases resulting from faulty genes, such as cystic fibrosis.

Off-the-shelf genes
Researchers have also developed techniques for introducing genes into organisms very early in their development, at the fertilized egg or early embryo stage. In the early 1980s, plasmid DNA containing a gene for growth hormone (a chemical that controls body growth) was added to mouse eggs just after they had been fertilized by mouse sperm. The developing embryos were put into female mice and allowed to develop. The resulting

"transgenic" mice grew larger than their siblings who lacked extra gene copies. It may be possible to use similar procedures in farm animals, to give more milk or meat.

The availability of genes "off the shelf", which can be altered and moved to new organisms, has many advantages. One example is making the hormone insulin. Many people with diabetes depend on insulin, which was formerly purified from the carcasses of pigs or cattle. By analyzing the human gene for making insulin, researchers were able to create it synthetically. They used plasmid vectors to add the gene to *E. coli* bacteria, which then made large quantities of insulin.

The genetically engineered insulin is not without its drawbacks, however. In some people it gives less warning of hypoglycemia (an attack caused by low blood sugar), and the consequent need to inject insulin. Genetic engineers may be able to alter the gene slightly to produce "designer insulin" that will reduce or remove this potentially dangerous side effect.

Genetic engineering has made it possible to make considerable quantities of human growth hormone, which was formerly very scarce and expensive. Treatment with the purified hormone can overcome a tendency to slow growth in children. Factor VIII, the missing blood-clotting chemical in the bleeding disease hemophilia, is now produced in a similar way. Interferon, a body chemical with potential uses as an anti-viral and anti-cancer agent, is another example. Transgenic tomatoes, with increased shelf life, have been produced using genetic engineering techniques.

The polymerase chain reaction
A powerful tool used by genetic engineers and molecular biologists is the *polymerase chain reaction* (PCR). The PCR uses an enzyme known as *DNA polymerase*, obtained from the heat tolerant microbe *Thermophilus aquaticus* which can live in hot springs. This enzyme naturally builds double-stranded (double-helix) DNA from a single-stranded DNA template. The PCR can "amplify" short lengths of DNA, making large quantities from a tiny starting amount.

The building, or synthesis, can be controlled and manipulated by adding short extra segments of DNA called *primers*. These stick onto the piece of template DNA, and initiate the reaction. By designing these synthetic primers carefully, and choosing the sites at which they stick, researchers can make large amounts of double-stranded DNA during the reaction.

The PCR takes place in a series or chain of repeated cycles. Each cycle involves separating the strands of template DNA by heating to 203° F (95° C), then cooling them to allow the primers to bind to them. The temperature is held at 162° F (72° C) for a short time, to allow the polymerase to work, as it makes double-stranded DNA from the single strands and a collection of DNA building-block nucleotide bases. Then the temperature is raised, the double strands separate, and the cycle begins again. As many as 25-30 cycles may be carried out in a typical reaction. The resulting DNA fragments may then be further analyzed. PCR has found particular use in the genetic fingerprinting techniques of FORENSIC SCIENCE.

Once a gene has been copied and amplified, and its chemical code determined, PCR can be used for *site-directed mutagenesis*. Instead of a primer being perfectly matched to the DNA template, it carries an altered code. After several amplification cycles, this altered stretch of DNA is put back into the original gene, altering or mutating it. In a living organism, the changed gene may produce more efficient enzymes tailored to particular tasks, such as dealing with oil and other environmental pollutants. This is one area of future research for the genetic engineers.

Cloning antigens

Immunization is an important means of combating infectious diseases – those due to bacteria or viruses. The person is given a vaccine against a disease, and the body reacts by becoming immune or resistant to it without actually suffering from the disease. Vaccines are given against pertussis (whooping cough), diphtheria, tetanus, polio, and several other diseases.

Many vaccines contain weakened (attenuated) or killed forms of the viruses or bacteria. These stimulate the body's defenses, as though the viruses or bacteria were invading. In the future, cloning tiny parts of the germs, specifically the proteins from their surface coating or "skin", should offer safer alternatives.

The pieces of protein coat in question are antigens that stimulate the body's immune system. With genetic engineering techniques, these proteins can be grown on their own, rather than attached to their viruses or bacteria. The antigen-only vaccine is therefore free of potentially dangerous viruses or bacteria, yet is just as efficient at stimulating immunity.

The hepatitis B virus infects the liver, sometimes causing very serious illness. An effective vaccine based on one of its surface proteins, HBsAg, has been developed using gene cloning techniques. A similar approach may help in the fights against AIDS and malaria.

Below: A diagram illustrating the polymerase chain reaction, a vital process in genetic engineering. The reaction, which results from the introduction of an enzyme known as DNA polymerase, is a cyclical process. In the first stage, the DNA is heated to separate the two strands and extra DNA segments called primers are attached. In the second stage the temperature is lowered and, as the enzyme takes effect, each strand of DNA splits into two. The temperature is then raised again, causing each new strand to split into two. This cycle is repeated as man as 25 to 30 times until the desired number of copied DNA strands is reached.

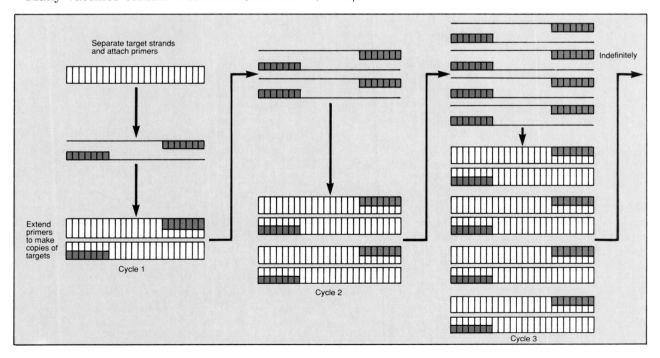

Genetics

Genetics is the study of inheritance – how physical features, characteristics, and even behavior are passed from parent to offspring. People have long been intrigued by the subject, especially the way inherited features, known as traits, run in families.

The gene is the basic unit of inheritance. Genes exist as segments of a very long, twisted, ladder-like chemical molecule called deoxyribonucleic acid or DNA, found in living cells. A gene is now understood to be a segment of DNA that contains the instructions, as a chemical code, to produce a specific protein. Proteins are central to the structure and workings of all cells.

In a living cell, DNA is coiled within one or more pairs of thread-shaped structures called chromosomes. Research into DNA, chromosomes, and the way genes work, is central to MOLECULAR BIOLOGY and GENETIC ENGINEERING.

Making gene maps

The entire set of genes in an organism is known as its genome. In the human being, for example, there are between 50,000 and 100,000 genes, tightly packed into 23 pairs of chromosomes. The huge human genome project aims to map all genes on the human chromosomes. A helpful advance in this area is the technique of chromosome in situ hybridization. This is a technique for getting labeled chromosomes (using a radioactive or fluorescent dye) to match up with other chromosomes in a cell or a laboratory preparation. The degree of matching or hybridization shows how similar or complementary the chromosomes (or the DNA in the chromosomes) are. Very simply, the most similar chromosomes stick together.

Chromosome mapping will help to diagnose inherited or genetic diseases, to gain a greater understanding of how genes work, and to replace defective genes with normal ones, thereby treating genetic disorders.

In the U.S., one baby in 25 has a disorder caused by abnormal genes. Many of these can be detected by taking samples at an early stage, when the baby is developing in the mother's uterus, and examining the chromosomes. If there is an abnormality, the mother may be offered a termination (abortion).

When a couple has a very high risk of conceiving a baby with a genetic disorder, it is now possible to carry out the in vitro or "test tube baby" procedure (see OBSTETRICS AND GYNECOLOGY). At a very early stage, the embryo is just a tiny ball of cells. One cell is removed, and its DNA is extracted and analyzed by techniques such as the polymerase chain reaction (see GENETIC ENGINEERING) and

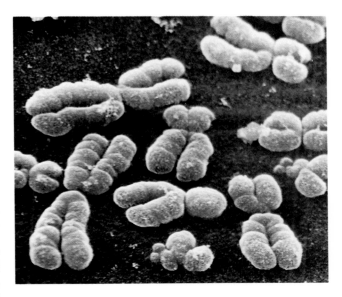

Above: Scanning electron micrograph of chromosomes. Each one has two strands joined at the center, a region known as the centromere or kinetochore, which splits when cell division takes place, thus providing half of each chromosome to the new pair of cells.

Below: Each human has 46 chromosomes, arranged in 23 pairs. These are normal female chromosomes; male chromosomes would have XY instead of two X chromosomes.

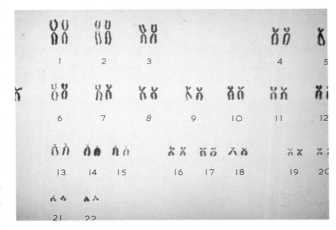

restriction enzymes (described below). If the results are clear, the ball of cells is implanted in the mother's uterus, and pregnancy begins.

Restriction enzymes are proteins that provide a new method for mapping genes on a chromosome. They cut or digest DNA at specific sites into tiny fragments. There are more than 200 known restriction enzymes, and each cuts DNA only at a certain point. The resulting pattern of DNA fragments can be identified by standard laboratory methods such as gel electrophoresis.

The pattern of DNA fragments varies from person to person, because each of us is unique, with our own combination of genes. A change in the DNA, due to genes being lost, added, or changed, results in a different pattern. Such changed patterns are called Restriction Fragment Length Polymorphisms, or RFLPs. Being bits of genes, they can be traced within a family.

Researchers used RFLPs to locate the genes for inherited disorders such as Huntington's disease, cystic fibrosis, and Duchenne muscular dystrophy. RFLPs are also the basis for genetic fingerprinting (see FORENSIC MEDICINE).

Will it be possible to treat or cure inherited disorders? The idea of gene therapy is becoming a reality. The defective gene could be replaced by a healthy version. However, the new gene must only be put into the body cells where it is required, or it may cause more damage. Also, the technique should not harm the receiving, or host, cells.

September 1990 saw the first gene therapy trial: in the U.S., a patient with a rare inherited illness, ADA deficiency, received healthy ADA genes carried by tailored retroviruses. These viruses had their own genes removed or altered, so they could not spread or multiply. The retrovirus added its new gene to the host cell's DNA, and produced the missing ADA. First results indicated the inserted ADA gene works for the life of the host cell, which could be months or years.

Another carrier, or vector, for therapeutic genes is the adenovirus that normally produces a common cold. In this case the virus does not add its gene into the host cell, but harmlessly infects the cell. In recent experiments, adenoviruses were delivered by a fine spray into rats' lungs, and succeeded in bringing the gene that corrects the lung disorder cystic fibrosis. The gene was still active six weeks later. Human trials may begin soon.

Choosing sex

Sex determination – male and female – is controlled by genes. Males and females generally have the same number of chromosomes, in matched pairs. But in the male, the members of one pair are different. These are the sex chromosomes. From their shapes, they are named XX in females and XY in males.

In 1991 geneticists isolated a single-gene fragment of the Y chromosome for humans and mice, and claimed it was the "sex gene". They named it SRY (human) or sry (mouse), for Sex-determining Region of the Y chromosome. When sry was introduced into female mouse embryos, they developed male sex organs. This indicates the sry gene is a "sex switch", making a genetic female develop male sex organs.

Other genes must also play a role in development, leading to a complete male body rather than a female one. With the latest genetic techniques, scientists may identify them. It may eventually be possible to choose a baby's sex by genetic means.

Below: In-situ hybridization, a technique for matching chromosomes labeled with a dye as a cell splits. The degree of matching shows how similar the chromosomes are. The labeling shows the position of the gene on a particular chromosome.

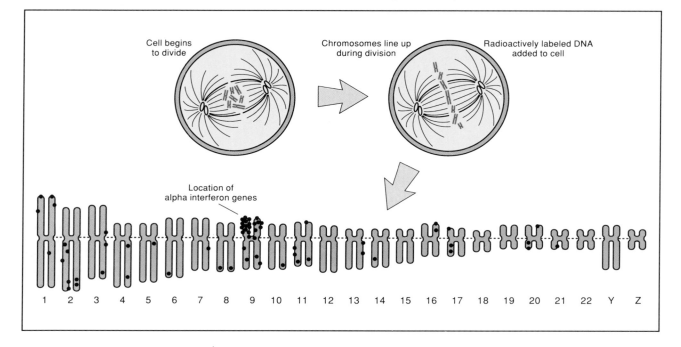

Cell begins to divide — Chromosomes line up during division — Radioactively labeled DNA added to cell

Location of alpha interferon genes

1 2 3 4 5 6 7 8 9 10 11 12 13 14 15 16 17 18 19 20 21 22 Y Z

Geochemistry

Geochemistry is the science which applies the principles of geology and chemistry to Earth materials. Many Earth science studies, from the evolution of the planet to the exploration for oil or precious metals, involve geochemistry. The subject can be broadly divided into low temperature geochemistry – concerned with soils and sediments – and high temperature geochemistry, which deals with rocks which have undergone heat treatment. High temperature systems can often be the more accurately modeled, but it is the low temperature research which is currently receiving the most attention.

In the latter field, many recent advances have been made by taking into account the effects of organic matter (micro and macro, living and dead), in a sub-discipline which is known as biogeochemistry. In addition, the application of low temperature geochemistry to current environmental problems ("environmental geochemistry") is a growth area for research.

Geochemical mapping
Once such features as the soils and sediments of a region have been sampled, they are analyzed to reveal the elements present. The next step is to make geochemical maps of the region. These are very useful, not just for mineral exploration, but also for studies of the relationship between geochemistry and health. They can highlight areas of pollution or trace element deficiencies. The geochemical map of China provides a dramatic exam-

ple of the way in which geochemistry and health can be related. It shows that selenium-rich sediment is widespread in the southwestern part of Hubei Province, where both humans and livestock in the area suffer from hair and nail loss caused by an excess of selenium. It has been clearly demonstrated that the selenium contained in soil, drinking water, crops, and vegetables originated directly, or indirectly from seleniferous rocks.

In 1988 a proposal for an International Geochemical Mapping Project was accepted by UNESCO/INGS (International Union of Geological Sciences). So far, good data are available for only a few elements and for less than 20 per cent of the world's land surface. This leaves 40 million sq miles (106.9 million sq km) still to be covered,

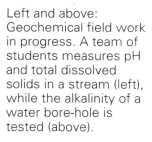

Left and above: Geochemical field work in progress. A team of students measures pH and total dissolved solids in a stream (left), while the alkalinity of a water bore-hole is tested (above).

Left: A demonstration of the role played by bacteria in the geochemistry of iron. The tube on the right has been sterilized and is uniform in color. The tube on the left has not been sterilized. The actions of micro-organisms in different parts of the tube affecting the iron's mobility and oxidation has led to the development of different colored regions in the tube.

excluding Antarctica! One hot topic at the moment is how widely spaced the sampling for the remaining area should be. A density of one sample per 100,000 sq km has been suggested, but experts disagree as to the value of such a wide spacing. The subject continues to be debated and a list of recommendations will be published in 1993. A major U.S. contribution to the International Geochemical Mapping project has been the preparation of data sets in CD-ROM (compact disc) format; this could be the ideal medium for storing all future reference data.

Analytical geochemistry

Geochemistry relies on fast and accurate analytical techniques for its success. One of the most significant analytical developments in decades is the ICP-MS (inductively coupled plasma-mass spectrometry). The sample is first vaporized to form a plasma – a hot, highly ionized gas which reaches temperatures of up to 11,000° K. Such a high temperature dissociates the sample into ions; the mass spectrum of the ions is measured using a quadruple mass spectrometer.

Most elements in the periodic table can be determined, though not hydrogen, helium, carbon, nitrogen, neon, or argon. The analysis takes less than one minute for over 90 elements, with concentrations as low as tens of parts per trillion. Isotope ratios are also easily determined. One recent advance is the use of lasers to vaporize very small and specific areas from thin sections of rocks, which can then be analyzed by ICP-MS.

From crystals to mountains

High temperature geochemistry has recently shown how the history of huge mountain belts can be unlocked from the study of tiny garnet crystals with a diameter no bigger than $1/16$ in. (1.5 mm). Garnets within altered sedimentary rocks from

Sulitjelma, north Norway, have already indicated a heating rate and a burial rate; in this case 15.5° F (8.6° C) and 0.5 mile (0.8 km) per million years. The work constitutes a significant advance in geochemistry since precise dating of garnet, combined with modern geothermometry and geobarometry, has now enabled scientists to define the pressure-temperature-time history of metamorphic rocks. Once the heating and cooling rate of mountain belts is known, the processes responsible for their origin can be deduced.

Bacteria and metals

For a long time it was not realized how much microorganisms can influence low temperature geochemistry. Now there is a huge surge of interest in this field.

One important area of such biogeochemical research is in understanding the sedimentary geochemistry of iron. Iron is a key constituent of Earth materials, being the fourth most abundant element in the Earth's crust and vital for the metabolism of plants and animals.

Certain bacteria, for example, can produce hydrogen disulfide from naturally occurring sulfates. This then converts iron oxy-hydroxides into iron sulfides, which play a significant part in the sedimentary cycle of iron.

A very recent and unexpected discovery by an international research team of sedimentary geochemists and microbiologists has proved that a bacterium called *Desulfovibrio* can produce iron directly – which could be significant when establishing how deposits of iron were formed.

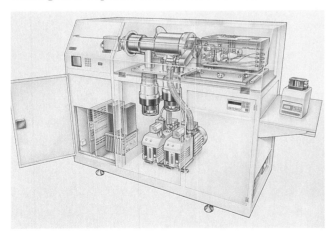

Above: ICP-MS machine, used to analyze rock samples. The gasified sample is pumped into the chamber at top right, where it is drawn into an argon plasma. The gray cylinder at center is the quadrupole mass spectrometer which separates the ions. These are then detected by the unit at top left and the results anaylzed by computer software.

Geography

Traditionally, geography divides into physical geography – the study of the world's natural features and processes – and human geography – the way people cover the world. But the current interest in environmental issues has linked the two, with the realization that the environmental problems we face almost always have both a physical and a human dimension. Modern technology has come to the rescue in helping to link them and to make sense of the huge amounts of data involved.

Work on tropical deforestation shows how these links apply. Tropical forests differ from temperate forests in that almost all the nutrients are held in the standing stock of trees, with very few being held in the soil. This means that once the trees are removed from a tropical rain forest, usually by logging, most of the nutrients are removed as well. The heavy rains of tropical areas soon wash the remaining nutrients away, taking with them any chance of forest regeneration.

In temperate forests, a much larger proportion of the nutrients are held in the humus-rich soil, so that even if the trees are removed it is usually possible for the forest to regenerate in time. The physical geographer can help predict what will happen when a forest is cleared.

On the local scale, there is soil erosion and siltation of reservoirs and waterways to consider, while globally the complex interactions of the climate have to be included in the equation.

On the human level, the geographer needs to study the social and economic pressures which are leading to deforestation in tropical countries. These countries, many of which are termed developing countries on account of their relatively low income per head of population, require more land for development as populations grow and "hard" overseas currency for international trade. Often the situation is further complicated by the need to pay interest on debts owed to banks in richer countries. Faced with such compelling needs, developing countries in tropical areas often have no alternative but to allow their forest stock to be destroyed.

New techniques in geography

New technological advances mean that geographers can now study more problems than ever before. Improved computer systems allow data such as soil, topography, and vegetation maps, to be stored, manipulated, and displayed on screen. These are known as Geographical Information Systems, which enable maps to be updated very rapidly. They can also combine and analyze information from different sources. For example, soil

Above: Satellite images are used in conjunction with information gathered at ground level to help interpret what they show. The blue lines in this image of the Brazilian rainforest reveal deforestation on a huge scale. The farmers burn the trees to release their nutrients into the soil, then move on when the soil is exhausted.

maps can be integrated with topographic and rainfall maps to find areas where clay soils, steep slopes, and high rainfall combine to create a high risk of landslides.

Geographical Information Systems can handle efficiently the large amounts of data produced by modern instruments. The work in 1991 on the siting of the United States Superconducting Super Collider (SSC) used several different datasets in this way. The SSC is an advanced particle accelerator housed in an elliptical underground tunnel 53 miles (85 km) in circumference, designed to research into the basic structure of matter. Several different factors had to be taken into account when choosing the location of such a large research facility.

First and foremost, the land had to be suitable for tunneling, so a place with stable geological conditions had be be found from geological maps. Also, to make sure that the extra staff would have nearby housing with good communications, information on regional resources had to be considered. Details of utilities had to be included as well, since the SSC requires ample supplies of electricity, water, and waste disposal facilities. Ecological and other geographical data were added to make sure that the development had the least effect on the local environment.

A Geographical Information System combined all this information so that various scenarios could be tried out on screen before the best location for the SSC was finally chosen.

Information from space

Remote sensing uses electromagnetic sensors and cameras to observe the earth from aircraft or satellites. Meteorological satellites have been providing images of the earth for use in weather forecasting since the 1960s. They provide an archive of data which can reveal how the earth's surface and climate are changing over time.

Increasingly sophisticated sensors carried on board modern satellites enable us to learn even more about what is going on in the world. Multispectral scanners sense energy coming up from the earth in different wavelengths. Some sense visible light, some sense invisible reflected solar radiation at infrared wavelengths, and some sense thermal

energy being emitted by the earth in the far infrared. All of these forms of energy can be displayed as color pictures that show features on the surface (such as the distribution of vegetation types) or in the atmosphere (such as cloud distribution).

Often cloud obscures the surface features which the geographer is interested in. However, there are now satellites that carry radar, which can "see" through cloud, to collect images in all weathers. This is particularly useful for remote sensing in tropical low pressure belts and high latitude areas, which are frequently cloud-covered.

Remote sensing images are used to map the distribution of surface cover types, such as forests, ice caps, deserts, and urban areas. As satellites orbit they pass over most parts of the Earth again and again, collecting a series of images over time. This allows geographers to monitor changes, such as the shrinking of ice caps or the growth of deserts in response to a warmer climate, providing a new way of measuring the rates of global environmental change.

Left and above: Geographical Information Systems allow data to be stored, manipulated, and displayed easily and quickly on screen.

Geology

The topics of radioactive waste and groundwater, dinosaurs and nuclear winter, and Antarctica and western North America seem to be unrelated. Yet to a geologist, a person who studies the Earth, the connections are clear. Each pairing concerns a major geological problem.

Geologists draw upon many other sciences (physics, biology, BOTANY, mathematics, chemistry, ZOOLOGY, ANATOMY, and astronomy), as well as allied earth sciences (OCEANOGRAPHY, LIMNOLOGY, HYDROLOGY, GEOCHEMISTRY, and GEOPHYSICS). Yet, the starting point for these problems is the same, the material of which the planet Earth is made – rocks. Rocks provide the record of Earth's history, and geology starts with mapping their distribution and the way they lie.

10,000-year stability

A critical area for geologic mapping is Yucca Mountain, Nevada, the location mandated by Congress for site characterization as the nation's high-level nuclear waste repository. The Department of Energy (DOE) must determine the site's suitability for a repository that will last 10,000 years. DOE will build and operate the repository, under license from the Nuclear Regulatory Commission, if a favorable decision is reached. The lithologies (types of rocks) found at the site, their structural setting, and physical properties will be crucial to this decision.

Yucca Mountain is within the Death Valley-Pancake Range volcanic zone of the Basin and Range Province. The proposed repository would be created within rocks laid down 10 to 15 million years ago in the Middle Miocene period.

The local rock – tuff – is a volcanic material that was originally deposited as an ash. Over time this has been compacted – that is, turned into rock. The region sits amid a system of north-south geological faults, many of which occurred about 12 million years ago, with minor movement since then. The proposed site for the repository is within a 1650-2450 ft (500-750 m) thick sequence that sits 650-1300 ft (200-400 m) above the present day water table.

A key concern is that the site should be isolated from flowing water. Groundwater traveling through the repository could pick up radioactivity from the stored materials and contaminate aquifers used for drinking water. But geologists have found that there are many hydrogenic – that

Below: Yucca Flats, Nevada, site of underground nuclear tests. Geological tests are determining whether nearby Yucca Mountain is suitable as a repository for nuclear waste.

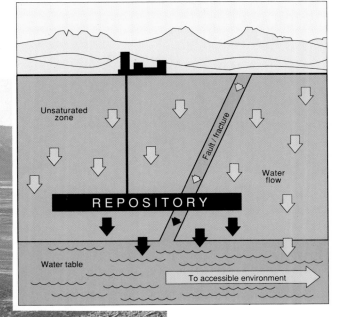

Above: Cross section of the geology of Yucca Mountain, Nevada, showing the relationship between water-bearing strata and the proposed nuclear waste repository.

Below: A selection of tektites – rock particles which originated from extraterrestrial bodies such as meteors. These provide evidence of asteroid contact with the Earth, a factor which, as recent research suggests, was to blame for the disappearance of the dinosaurs. Scientists in 1992 discovered a possible impact site in Yucatan, Mexico. Tektites of the same age have been found throughout the Gulf of Mexico and Haiti.

Above: Meteor or asteroid impact, such as that which is believed to have led to the extinction of dinosaurs, creates similar conditions to those proposed in "nuclear winter" scenarios developed by climatologists. Major volcanic eruptions, such as this one on New Island, Iceland, also create nuclear winter conditions.

Traces of a cataclysm

Geologic mapping is used to unravel mysteries of the Earth's past, as well as solving modern problems, such as the one at Yucca Mountain. The great geological mystery of why dinosaurs became extinct at the end of the Cretaceous period (65 million years ago) may be near a solution because geologists map the distribution of rocks vertically as well as horizontally.

In 1980 Walter Alvarez and co-workers suggested that an asteroid 6 miles (10 km) in diameter struck the Earth and sent up a dust cloud that blanketed the earth in darkness, disrupted the food chain by stopping photosynthesis, and caused an episode of global cooling. This led to the sudden demise of 52 per cent of all species on Earth, but affected land-based organisms most with an 81 per cent extinction rate, including all the dinosaurs. The conditions created by such an impact would be very similar to those proposed in "nuclear winter" scenarios which are studied by climatologists.

The clue that led Alvarez to put forward his controversial suggestion was a surprisingly high amount of the element iridium in the layers of rocks which mark the boundary between the Cretaceous and the Tertiary periods – known as

is, water-related – mineral deposits in the area. The question is whether these deposits were created by hot subterranean water, linked with volcanic activity up to two million years ago, moving upward, or rainfall percolating downward.

One DOE report suggested there is a good deal of evidence that the site's groundwater level was once much higher and could rise again. Research in CLIMATOLOGY shows that the area has become more arid in the last 10,000 years. A DOE internal review committee could not agree about the evidence, but a National Academy of Sciences panel held that there was not much risk of groundwater getting into the repository. The issue has not been resolved and geologists are now in the process of mapping zones of high permeability through which water might pass.

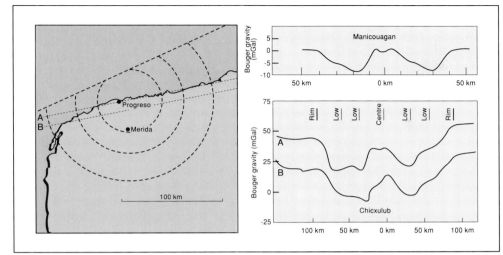

Left: Evidence for a major meteorite crater or astrobleme at Chicxulub in the Yucatán peninsula comes from gravity readings, profiled along lines A and B (here separated by 25 units for clarity). The profile of the Manicouagan crater, a known astrobleme, is shown for comparison.

Right: Geological deposits around the Gulf of Mexico suggest that the Chicxulub event dates from the same time as the K-T boundary, when a mass extinction occurred which ended the age of the dinosaurs on Earth.

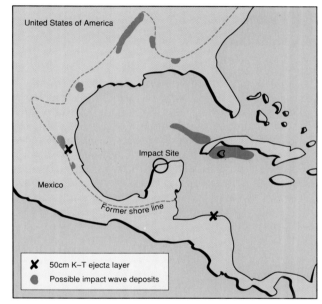

the K-T boundary. Iridium is rare on Earth but more common in asteroids and meteors. The idea has attracted so much attention since it was proposed that more than 2500 books and papers related to it have been published.

In their efforts to prove or disprove the hypothesis, geologists have mapped iridium anomalies in K-T boundary rocks in many parts of the world. They have found several other pieces of evidence pointing to a major impact at that time. Rocks of this age also contain such features as tektites (silicate glass spherules which appear to have spent some time in space), shock metamorphosed quartz (which forms only under extremely high pressure), and the effects of tsunami (seismic sea waves), which would have followed an impact. A mounting body of evidence in favor of the impact hypothesis was built but the crucial evidence, the impact crater itself, remained hidden.

Direct evidence of the impact may, however, have been found. The August 14, 1992 issue of *Science* published a report showing that the 113 mile (180 km) wide Chicxulub crater (Yucatán Peninsula, Mexico), originally located using magnetic and gravity anomaly maps, was the same age as the K-T boundary. This location fits nicely with tektites of this age found in Haiti, northern Mexico, and Ocean Drilling Project boreholes in the Gulf of Mexico. Alvarez was quoted by *Science* as saying, "It looks...like...the smoking gun".

However, many geologists still do not fully accept the impact hypothesis. Some suggest that intense volcanic activity played a role, noting that volcanism can put large amounts of ash and dust into the atmosphere and that at the same time as the K-T boundary there was extensive volcanic activity which formed the huge Deccan Trap in India. Work in PALEONTOLOGY shows that many of the extinctions were gradual, not sudden, and were probably related to falling sea level and episodes of oceanic oxygen starvation. They see the impact as a possible coup de grace, not an underlying cause of the extinction.

SWEAT

The plate tectonics revolution of the 1960s showed that because Earth's lithosphere (outer shell) is mobile, the continents change their positions and oceans are created and destroyed. This forced geologists to produce a new type of map – paleogeographic maps that show the positions of continents at various times in Earth history. These use both

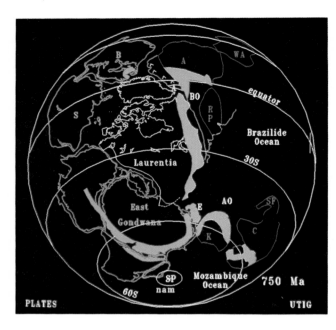

Above: Reconstruction of the early to mid Neopterozoic supercontinent, showing Laurentia – the core of modern day North America – was joined to East Antarctica, Australia, and South America, themselves parts of Gondwanaland. Laurentia later split from the supercontinent, opening the Pacific basin. The SWEAT theory suggests that what is now North America's West Coast was once joined to what is now Antarctica. On the map, "A" is Amazonia, the core of modern day South America; "AB" is Arequipa-Baltica; "C" is the Congo craton; "E" is part of modern West Antarctica; "K" is the Kalahari craton; "RP" is the Rio de la Plata craton, part of modern South America's west coast; "S" is Siberia; "WA" is the West African craton.

lithological data found on modern geological maps and paleomagnetic data. PALEOMAGNETISM is a technique used to find out the latitude at which a rock formed in the geological past. Paleogeographic mapping may provide the solution to another geological problem, one that involves rocks more than 500 million years old.

The rocks of the Windemere Group extend from northern Canada to southeastern California. They formed between 570 million and one billion years ago at the edge of a former supercontinent as it broke apart and a new ocean formed. The problem vexing geologists who study the Windemere rocks is to find their counterpart; that is, the rocks deposited on the other side of that ocean. This is more than just an academic exercise in reconstructing Earth history. There may be economic consequences as continental margin rocks are often prolific sources of gas and oil.

In 1991 two geologists, Eldridge Moores and Ian Dalziel, independently proposed that the counterparts of the Windemere rocks would be found in East Antarctica. The hypothesis became known as the Southwest U.S.-East Antarctica (SWEAT) connection and was built upon two main foundations: the similarity in geological histories and the paleomagnetic position of these areas between 500 and 750 million years ago.

SWEAT had barely been proposed before controversy started to erupt. Paleontologists were quick to point out that Cambrian (510-570 million year old) faunas of Antarctica are unlike those of western North America. Other geologists quickly realized that implications drawn from the SWEAT reconstruction contradict the geological history of (then) adjacent regions.

In the time since it was proposed, a series of publications related to SWEAT has appeared. Whether or not the hypothesis is viable, it seems likely to provoke a response similar to the impact hypothesis and generate a great deal of research. Geologic mappers will be in business for some considerable time to come.

Geology to the rescue

Geologists have recently solved a dilemma that has been baffling zoologists ever since Charles Darwin explored the Galapagos Islands, about 500 miles (800 km) off the coast of Ecuador, in 1835.

The islands are so remote from other land that many of the creatures on them have developed separately from those on the mainland. The discoveries that Darwin made there led him to propose his famous theory of evolution. But despite the success of this theory in explaining how all types of creatures have evolved over long periods of time, there is a difficulty with applying the theory to the Galapagos.

These islands are volcanic in origin, and can have existed for no more than three million years. Work in molecular biology shows that this is far too short a time for the marine iguanas on the islands to have diverged from their mainland cousins – they would have needed 15 to 20 million years in order to be as different as they actually are.

But in 1992 a team of geologists at Oregon State University published the results of an underwater survey which showed that the present islands, though they only appeared no more than three million years ago, are part of a chain which has been in existence for much longer. The older ones have now been worn away, but are presumably the ones around which the ancestors of the present marine iguanas lived. So evolution would have had millions of years to produce the differences between mainland and island creatures which Darwin observed.

Geophysics

It is 3940 miles (6371 km) to the center of the Earth and our deepest borehole only reaches to 7½ miles (12 km) from the surface. Nevertheless, geophysicists have explored the interior of our planet very effectively. They have discovered the structure and composition of the Earth by remote sensing techniques; that is, by observing the passage of seismic waves through it, and by measuring its electrical, magnetic, thermal, and gravity properties.

Exploration geophysicists use these same techniques to search for oil, gas, water, and other vital minerals, to search for alternative energy sources and to assist environmental scientists to discover toxic or hazardous waste fluids in the ground. Geophysicists are trained in mathematics, physics, and GEOLOGY, and their tasks range from using instruments in the field to determining the position of an oil well.

Oil and gas exploration

At the moment we have inexpensive energy from plentiful oil and gas supplies. Unfortunately, the population of the world is rising very rapidly, having doubled from 2½ billion to five billion people in the past 50 years, with a consequent increase in demand for energy from these fuels. At the present rate of world consumption of three billion tons of oil each year, all the known reserves will be exhausted by the year 2025. Exploration geophysicists are under great pressure to find new oil reservoirs, and they are searching for the remaining, smaller reserves in increasingly hostile environments.

Geophysicists have been very successful in finding these smaller oil fields, and the proportion of successful discoveries to every 100 boreholes drilled has doubled during the past ten years. This has been achieved by constantly improving the techniques used to explore for oil and gas reservoirs.

Oil and gas are "fossil fuels" – they originated millions of years ago as decaying organic remains. As the ground surface was buried under an increasing thickness of the sediments, the combined effect of high temperature and high pressure turned the sediments into rock and the organic remains into oil and gas. They found their way upwards until they were trapped in porous sandstones beneath an impermeable "cap-rock". Oil and gas sandstone reservoirs occur at depths from the surface down to 3 miles (5 km). Unfortunately, there are no geophysical techniques which will detect oil and gas directly at great depths, but from experience geophysicists know that the sandstone reservoir rocks often have a characteristic structure or shape which they can detect using seismic waves. The geophysicist's role is to use these waves to map the sub-surface rocks as accurately as possible.

The basic idea of the method is simple. A source sends seismic waves (which are similar to sound waves) into the Earth. The seismic waves are reflected from the boundaries or interfaces between the different rock types such as sandstone, shale, and limestone. The reflected energy returns to the surface of the Earth, where it is detected by receivers and recorded by a computer on a magnetic tape or disk. The time of travel of the wave from the surface to the interface reveals the depth of the structure. By moving the shot and receivers from one position to another across the ground surface, scientists can map the variation in the depth of the interface in detail.

Originally, massive charges of explosives were used as the sources of seismic energy both at sea and on land. However, not only were these dangerous to handle but they caused severe damage to fish and to property. The modern source at sea uses a high pressure pulse of air from a tube or gun which safely produces a large energy seismic wave. On land, mechanical vibrators mounted on trucks are used to shake the ground surface, again producing a high energy seismic wave. Until

Right: The Pacific Horizon, a survey ship which was upgraded in 1992 to carry the most up-to-date equipment, carries out a three-dimensional seismic survey.

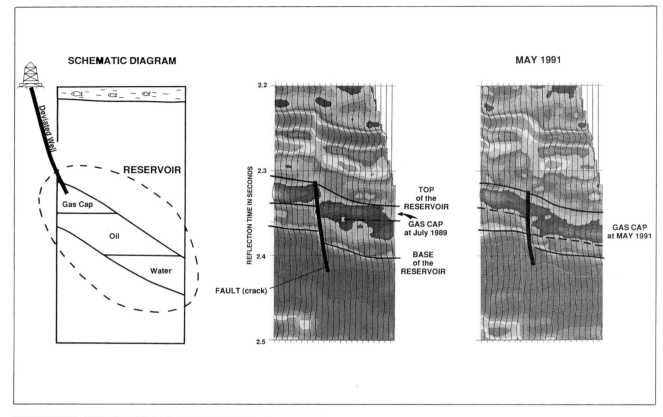

SCHEMATIC DIAGRAM

Deviated Well

RESERVOIR

Gas Cap

Oil

Water

FAULT (crack)

MAY 1991

REFLECTION TIME IN SECONDS

2.2

2.3

2.4

2.5

TOP of the RESERVOIR

GAS CAP at July 1989

BASE of the RESERVOIR

GAS CAP at MAY 1991

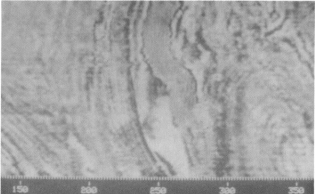

Above: An example of four-dimensional seismic surveying from the North Sea, off the eastern coast of the United Kingdom. These pictures show the changes – due to oil production – of a gas cap, which has been tapped by a deviated (non-vertical) well from 1989 to 1991. The difference in seconds between the locations of the gas cap indicates that by 1991 the cap was 145 ft (44 m) deeper than it was in 1989.

recently, geophysicists carried out the sub-surface investigation at sea by towing the seismic source and receivers in a straight line behind the ship. After processing the data the result was a seismic section, a flat picture of the geology beneath that particular surface line, down to a depth of about 3 miles (5 km).

You can get a good idea of what a seismic section looks like by imagining a picture of an enor-

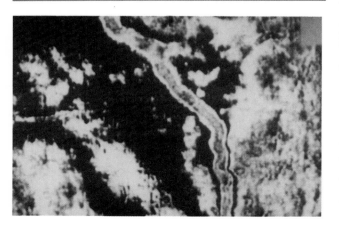

Left: Two views of the results of three-dimensional marine seismic surveys: Top: A 1.8 mile square section of the Irish Sea, obtained during a survey aimed at finding gas-bearing rock. A deep channel about 500 yards wide can be seen as a thick black line running up the center of the picture. Bottom: The meandering course of an ancient stream, now submerged, can be seen in this picture, which represents a section roughly 0.6 mile (1 km) square.

Above: Subsurface radar equipment. The radar is capable of reading both very shallow and very great depths, making it extremely useful for environmental protection and engineering work, where it is important to know what lies immediately beneath the surface.

Below: This cross section from subsurface radar equipment shows not only the profile of a lake bed but also structure in the bedrock beneath it.

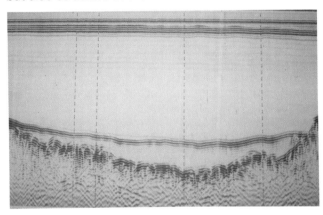

mous cliff; you see the beds of sedimentary rock running across the cliff face, giving the geology in that plane in very great detail. However, from this display you have no idea how the beds change behind the cliff face, and geophysicists have realized that it is necessary to obtain a complete image of the sub-surface geology by "shooting" in many different directions, not just in straight lines. The difference between the two surveying methods is that of trying to decide on the shape and structure of an object by viewing it from one position, compared to lifting it up and rotating it around in front of our eyes to pick up the subtle variations in form and shape.

Three-dimensional seismology

The new way of acquiring the seismic data is called three-dimensional reflection seismology.

The three-dimensional survey requires the geophysicist to shoot and receive at many different points, so powerful computers are required to plan the survey, to keep track of the positions of all the shots and receiver-points, and to process the seismic data to produce the three-dimensional image of the sub-surface geology.

Two factors have greatly helped geophysicists to carry out these surveys – the growth in the power of computers and the recent availability of satellite navigation systems. Over the past decade the processing power of supercomputers has been increased from an ability to carry out 200 million arithmetic calculations each second, to 10 billion such calculations. Computer experts believe that by 1995 these computers will be able to carry out 100 billion calculations each second. These astronomical numbers are difficult to comprehend, yet such power is needed to handle the enormous amount of seismic data which are continuously collected in the three-dimensional survey.

The growth of satellite navigation systems during the past decade has greatly helped marine surveys. The system of satellites circling the Earth means that the geographical position of the survey vessel, each shot point, and each seismic detector, can be determined every few seconds throughout the survey, with an accuracy of less than 10 ft (3 m), by means of a radio receiver no bigger than a pocket calculator.

Geophysicists store the three-dimensional seismic image of the Earth's sub-surface structure in a computer memory. The computer can be used to display the results in any form, as a series of cross sections like the cliff face, or as maps of the sediments at any depth in the Earth.

Four-dimensional seismology

Perhaps even more clever than three-dimensional seismology is the four-dimensional version, in which the seismic survey is repeated at regular intervals to observe the changes in the sub-surface over time – the fourth dimension. Using this technique geophysicists can tell oil reservoir engineers what is happening in the reservoir during production. All oil reservoirs have several wells drilled through them, so that the oil or gas can flow out of the reservoir and up to the surface.

Geophysicists place seismic sources in one well and seismic receivers in a separate one so they can measure the speed of the seismic waves through the reservoir. By combining the results from all the sources and all the receivers, the computer can create a seismic image of the reservoir as a large-scale version of the medical scans of the inside of a human being, using ultrasound. They allow reservoir engineers to see exactly what is going on inside the reservoir, and to judge the effectiveness of such techniques as using steam piped in to increase the temperature, and thus the "runniness" of the oil. Geophysicists are able to undertake and interpret these complex surveys because of the continuing growth in the power of computers, and the miniaturization of electronics which enables the sources and receivers to be sent down a 6 in (15 cm) bore hole.

The traditional role of geophysicists has been to make images of the Earth at great depths. During the past decade, geophysicists have become increasingly involved with undertaking very detailed shallow surveys in connection with environmental problems.

For instance, in the case where hazardous waste is buried at shallow depths, it may be dangerous to disturb the soil, and engineers call on the remote sensing techniques of geophysicists. In many such cases the hazardous waste is present within the ground water, and causes a change in the electrical properties of the water.

Geophysicists then use ground penetrating radar, a system exactly like radar used on ships and aircraft, but with the antenna pointing into the ground. The microwave electromagnetic pulse can penetrate to 160 ft (50 m) in dry soil and sand, but is rapidly absorbed by electrically conducting ground water.

The technique used is to pull the antenna across the ground region to be investigated; the equipment produces an "image" of the rock inter-faces. From the image the geophysicist can interpret the change from poorly conducting, uncontaminated ground water to highly conducting, contaminated ground water and thus plot the position of the contaminated zone.

Alternative energy sources

There is a finite amount of oil and gas and eventually this fruitful source of energy will run out. Geophysicists are looking at other sources of energy which exist within the Earth, and which may be able to make a contribution towards the total requirements of mankind. Igneous rocks, such as granite, which occur in many countries (for example, the Basin and Range Province in the southwest United States) contain significant amounts of the radioactive elements uranium, thorium, and potassium. The natural decay of these elements generates heat.

By drilling boreholes several miles into the granite, fracturing it, and then pumping water through the borehole/fracture system, boiling water can be obtained in large quantities. The system acts like a very low level, very safe, nuclear reactor with no hazardous by-products. Geophysicists have discovered that the important factor in the efficient heating of the water is the fracturing of the rock between the boreholes. This allows the water to flow freely, and gives a large surface area for transferring heat from the hot rock to the water.

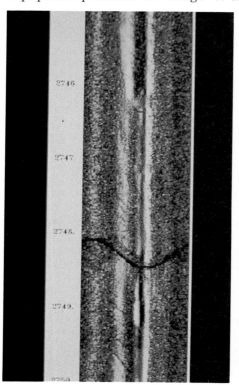
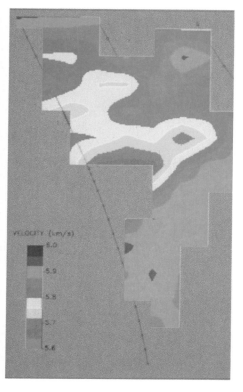

Left: A new energy source has recently been developed in the U.S. by passing drilling boreholes deep into radioactive granite and passing water through it. The picture on the far left is a borehole televiewer image of a fracture within the granite (shown as a black line). Water is passed through these fractures to extract heat from the granite. The depth of the borehole is given on the left. The picture on the left is a seismic velocity topogram of a region between wells through which water has been passed into fractured granite. The warmer the color indicates on the image, the more heat has been extracted from the granite.

Gerontology

It may be an unpalatable fact, but we are all aging all the time. From age 12 or 13, we decline slowly and steadily until we die, with no sudden increase in the rate of deterioration at the age of 60 or 65. Gerontology is the study of how aging takes place, and how to overcome its more distressing effects.

The ultimate biological marker of aging is an increase in the risk of death. As we age, we are less able to adapt to changes in our environment, whether they are external or internal to the body. A younger person is almost certainly better able to dodge a flying missile or a car that is out of control; his or her body can deal more effectively with a clot in an artery. Older people have slower reactions and less strength in their muscles. They are less able to survive assaults on their internal well-being, such as exposure to a cold environment or thirst.

Research has shown that the age at which the aging process starts is constant in all populations in which it has been studied. So is the maximum life span, at about 110 years. Claims that people in some mountain ranges live to 140 are myths.

Such constancy suggests that the onset of aging and the maximum life span are under genetic control. Recent studies have shown that there are indeed genes that help to control aging, probably by determining the accuracy with which the organism repairs damage to its cell constituents. Such repair is essential to correct the constant assaults by cosmic radiation, ultraviolet radiation, and the myriad chemical reactions that go on in every cell of the body. How long we live may therefore be determined by how efficiently our bodies can repair this kind of damage.

Until recently, all the genes that had been found to be involved with aging, in both humans and animals, had functions that accelerated the process. Then, a few years ago, scientists discovered a gene in the nematode worm, *Caenorhabditis elegans*, that prolongs its lifespan. Although most nematodes live for about two weeks, the lifespan of worms with this gene was increased by 60 per cent. It is not yet known if an equivalent gene exists in humans, nor what the gene's function is. It is possible that it assists the cellular repair processes.

No one would want a "gene transplant" to allow them to live for another 10 years if it meant suffering for longer with unpleasant conditions such as strokes and Alzheimer's disease. Yet the prospects for preventing many of the diseases of old age are good. Although it was once thought that they were genetically determined and that there was therefore nothing that could be done to avoid them, it is

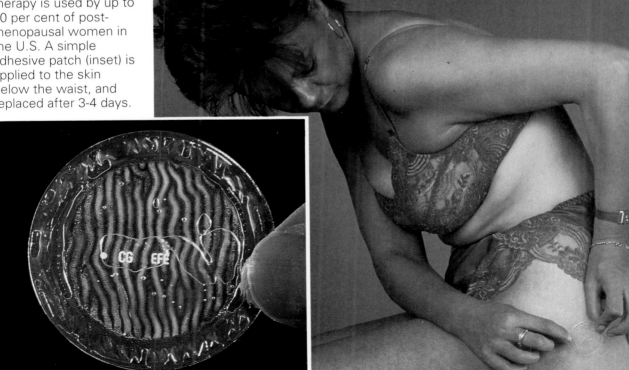

Right and below: Hormone replacement therapy is used by up to 40 per cent of post-menopausal women in the U.S. A simple adhesive patch (inset) is applied to the skin below the waist, and replaced after 3-4 days.

Left: Research shows that physical exercise can help people to live longer and feel better in old age. This jogger is 90 years old.

decline in mental abilities as they age, except commonly in the 12 months before death. The differences found in the earlier tests came about because older people come from what is essentially a different culture to younger people, because of their different educations and experiences. Most current research is now being conducted to take account of the cultural differences of older people, although older people still suffer much social discrimination because many people do not understand this distinction.

now known that environmental factors are largely to blame.

For example, many studies conducted over the past couple of decades have shown that components of the diet such as too much saturated fat, carcinogens, salt, and alcohol, are linked to diseases such as heart disease, cancer, high blood pressure, and strokes.

This is good news, as it is much easier to change your lifestyle than modify your genes. Healthier lifestyles will allow more people to achieve their genetic maximum lifespan. Population statistics show this is already happening: since the 1870s, the average lifespan has gone up enormously, while the maximum lifespan has not.

Recent studies have shown that some features of the aging process can even be reversed: people who take up physical exercise even at the age of 70 can recover approximately 15 per cent of their muscle strength.

The realization that environment and lifestyle often determine whether diseases develop in old age has had important ramifications for their prevention and treatment. For example, people are no longer denied most medical and surgical treatments purely on the grounds that they are too old. It is now recognized that it is physiology that counts, rather than age, and that old people can recover perfectly well from, for example, open heart surgery.

Studies which appeared to show that the mental functions of elderly people were less good than those of their younger counterparts have been largely discounted. More recent work has shown that individuals do not show a corresponding

• FACT FILE •

- It may one day be possible to delay or even prevent some of the changes in the body that come about during aging, by taking natural chemicals such as hormones. For example, some studies have suggested that elderly men suffering from muscle weakness may be deficient in growth hormone and that, if they take growth hormone, it builds and strengthens their muscles.

- Tests on how growth hormone can help delay the effects of aging are still in their infancy. Before the treatment could be made available, doctors would have to prove beyond a doubt that it was both safe and effective.

- Another hormonal treatment, hormone replacement therapy for women, is better established. Once a woman has passed the menopause, her ovaries stop producing estrogen. As a result, her risk of heart disease rises, as does her risk of developing osteoporosis (thinning of the bones). Osteoporosis can lead to bone fractures, most commonly of the hip, which can sometimes be fatal.

- Gerontologists have discovered that hormone replacement therapy can protect against osteoporosis and associated fractures, as well as reducing a woman's risk of a heart attack. There may be risks as well as benefits, however: some studies have shown an increased risk of breast cancer in women who are taking hormone replacement therapy.

Hematology

Hematology is the branch of PATHOLOGY concerned with diseases of the blood. These range from inherited disorders such as hemophilia and thalassemia to conditions such as leukemia, which can develop in childhood or later life.

Some hematologists work in blood transfusion services, helping to insure an adequate supply of infection-free blood for transfusion. Others are highly involved in caring directly for patients, some of whom may be severely ill with conditions such as leukemia.

The arrival of the human immunodeficiency virus (HIV) during the 1980s posed an enormous problem for blood transfusion services. Many people were infected through receiving contaminated blood products, such as the clotting factors used to treat hemophiliacs. Fortunately, highly accurate tests are now available to screen all blood donated for transfusion. Blood is discarded if it is found to be infected. In the U.S., Europe, and other developed countries that can afford to carry out such testing, transmission of HIV via infected blood transfusions or blood products is now virtually nonexistent. In 1992, a blood substitute was developed (see PHYSIOLOGY). After clinical trials, it should be valuable for infection-free transfusion.

Treating leukemia

One area where scientific and medical develop-ments have reaped enormous benefits for patients is in the treatment of leukemia by bone marrow transplantation.

There are several different types of leukemia. All of them involve excessive production of a certain type of blood cell. The multiplying cells never mature properly, which means they cannot carry out their normal functions, of which one of the most important is fighting infection.

Leukemia is treated with anti-cancer drugs and sometimes with radiation. The aim of treatment is to kill the leukemic cells while allowing the normal cells to survive. In some cases, bone marrow transplantation can give the patient a better chance of long term cure. The bone marrow donor must be matched carefully to the patient to avoid the risk of rejection. For this reason, marrow donors normally come from the patient's immediate family.

The procedure makes it possible for doctors to give intensive treatment with anti-cancer drugs or radiation or both. This would normally risk killing the patient by destroying his or her own bone marrow, along with the leukemic cells. But the patient is "rescued" by receiving the donated marrow, which replaces his or her own.

Today, of patients aged under 45 who have a bone marrow transplant from a related donor matched for compatibility, 50 to 60 per cent will still be alive five years later. Depending on the type of leukemia, the disease will eventually return in more than a third of patients, but these

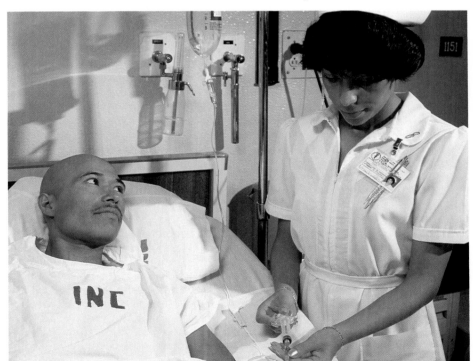

Left: Cytotoxic chemotherapy is often a successful treatment for widespread or secondary cancer. It involves the injection of drugs into the bloodstream and often causes nausea and vomiting. This patient is being administered an anti-emetic drug prior to chemotherapy. The drug is usually given by intravenous infusion into the bloodstream just before therapy, and by tablets thereafter. Severely emetogenic therapy may require additional intravenous dosages.

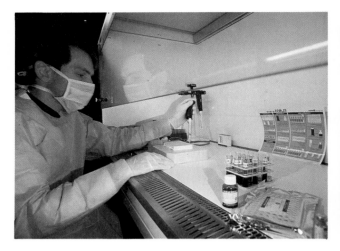

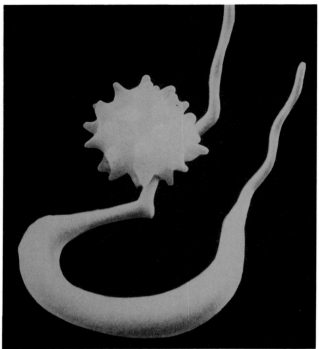

Above: Technician performing an ELISA (enzyme-linked immunosorbent assay) test for antibodies to HIV, the causative agent of AIDS.
Right: False-color scanning electron micrograph of the abnormal type of red blood cell that causes sickle-cell anemia.

results are still very good when it is considered that survival after diagnosis used to be measured in months.

Diagnostic techniques

Another important breakthrough in hematology has been the development of rapid tests to diagnose inherited disorders of the blood. For example, a test to diagnose sickle-cell disease now takes only 40 minutes.

Between 8 and 25 per cent of people of African and Afro-Caribbean origin carry the sickle-cell gene. Such carriers are perfectly healthy. But someone with two copies of the gene will suffer from sickle-cell disease. If two carriers have a child together, the child will have a one in four chance of having two copies of the gene and having sickle-cell disease. This may be fatal during childhood.

Many hematologists now work in clinics that provide genetic counseling for people at high risk of carrying such genes. Couples can find out if they both carry the gene for sickle-cell disease and the likelihood of their conceiving an infected child; if they do, they will be offered prenatal diagnosis when the woman becomes pregnant.

Early in pregnancy, an obstetrician can take a sample of the membranes produced by the developing fetus in a comparatively low risk procedure called chorionic villus sampling (see OBSTETRICS AND GYNECOLOGY). Even though only a tiny amount of tissue is obtained, the DNA in the sample can be amplified using a technique called the polymerase chain reaction (see GENETIC ENGINEER-

ING). Overnight, this provides enough DNA for the hematologist to analyze.

The test for the defective gene relies on the distinctive way in which an enzyme cuts the sequence of bases in the DNA. If two copies of the gene are present, the enzyme will cut the DNA molecule into a series of lengths of a particular size and quantity. If only one copy is present, or none, a different pattern of DNA pieces will result.

Using growth factors

The discovery of natural chemicals that stimulate bone marrow cells to mature into different types of blood cells allows doctors to give more effective treatment for cancer and some types of anemia.

The chemicals are called growth factors. Each one specifically stimulates a particular kind of blood cell to grow. For example, the growth factor called erythropoietin (EPO) stimulates red cells (erythrocytes) to grow; another, called GM-CSF, stimulates the growth of white cells.

Patients with cancer have been among the first to benefit from the use of growth factors. The drugs used to treat cancer often target not only the rapidly dividing cells of the tumor but also the cells of the bone marrow. If many cells of the bone marrow are killed, the patient may be unable to fight serious infections. With growth factors, doctors can give larger and more effective doses of anti-cancer drugs if they also give patients growth factors to help their normal bone marrow recover more quickly. When EPO is given to people with kidney failure they need fewer transfusions for anemia.

Homeopathy

Homeopathy is probably the best known type of "alternative medicine". It has not changed much since the original publication of the ideas behind it by the German physician Samuel Hahnemann nearly two centuries ago, but recently it has been at the center of a major scientific battle.

It is based on two principles. The first is that "like cures like": a disease can be cured by administering a substance which, when taken by a healthy person, causes symptoms similar to those of the disease itself – the basis of vaccination.

The second is more contentious: that it is possible to increase a substance's potency by diluting it many times and shaking it violently (a process called "succussion"). The medicine is diluted with alcohol or distilled water to produce a liquid, or mixed with lactose and then dried to produce a powdered solid. This idea confounds chemistry as we know it, for many homeopathic remedies are

alleged to be so dilute that not one molecule of the original substance remains. How, then, can there be any effects from it?

Before one tries to explain an effect, however, one has to make sure it exists. Do homeopathic remedies work as claimed? Many people say yes to that question. Like many of the other types of alternative medicine – herbalism, faith healing, aromatherapy, iridology, reflexology, and acupuncture – homeopathy claims many successes, drawing most of its evidence from the testimony of grateful customers.

Double-blind testing

This anecdotal type of evidence in support of homeopathy, however, is generally scientifically unacceptable. The difficulty is that taking a particular treatment and being cured is not the same as being cured by the treatment. Many illnesses will clear up spontaneously if left to themselves, or if they have a psychological component.

Medical drugs, therefore, are tested using "double-blind" controls (in which neither the patient nor the person administering the treatment knows whether it involves the real drug or a placebo). This procedure is intended to detect improvement in a condition which comes from the patient's belief in the treatment, rather than from the treatment itself. But supporters of homeopa-

Below: A homeopathic doctor's bag. Most homeopathic remedies are based on natural salts and extracts of minerals or plants. Some remedies, called "nosodes" are based on extracts of diseased tissues or bacteria. Remedies can be prepared as tinctures, granules, or powders.

thy often say that such testing does not work for homeopathic remedies because they are so personal. Conventional medicine treats the disease, they argue, while homeopathy treats the whole person.

However, scientific evidence which supports homeopathy is, naturally enough, not rejected. In 1988 the prestigious journal *Nature* shocked the science world by publishing a paper which appeared to lend support to homeopathy. Written by Jacques Benveniste, a pharmacologist at the French National Institute of Health and Medical Research, it reported on a series of experiments in which basophils, a type of white blood cells, reacted to an antibody solution. The solution was so dilute that it did not contain a single molecule of the original antibody. Benveniste's suggestion was that the molecules of the distilled water used in the solution might somehow have a "memory" of the antibody substance.

Follow-up

Nature was not content with simply publishing the paper. As a follow up, the journal sent a team of three investigators to examine Benveniste's results: James Randi, a magician and investigator of paranormal claims; John Maddox, the editor of

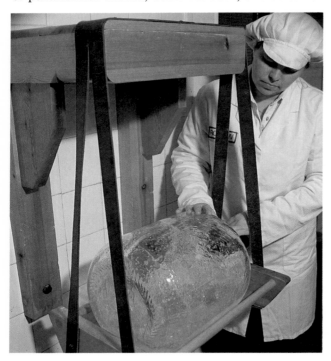

Above: Potentizing a homeopathic dilution. The preparation begins by obtaining the original substance in as pure a form as possible. It is subsequently diluted and shaken violently, as on this frame, which allows a large volume to be shaken by hand.

Nature; and Walter W. Stewart, an organic chemist and specialist in scientific fraud from the U.S. National Institute of Health.

The investigative team concluded that the researchers' methodology was flawed, and the results were not reproducible. In the scientific world, this is damning criticism: the basis of science is that independent researchers working in different labs should be able to get the same results if they repeat experiments using the same protocols. The controversy over Benveniste's research continues, however, as believers claim the investigation was biased.

A further analysis of tests of homeopathy was published in the *British Medical Journal* in February 1991. The authors surveyed over 100 published studies, of which three-quarters had found positive effects for homeopathy, while the rest had either found no positive effects, or were uninterpretable.

Believers tend to quote the positive results. But the authors' conclusion was that the majority of those studies were of poor quality and used questionable experimental designs. They also pointed out that "publication bias" is a problem: pro-homeopathy researchers may discard negative results as failures, and publish only the positive ones. The authors concluded by saying that even the well-designed studies had a non-trivial flaw. This report, too, continues to be assailed by supporters of homeopathy.

Such scientific criticisms do not in general affect homeopathy's popularity. Throughout the 19th century, homeopathy spread, traveling from Europe to the U.S. Here it reached a peak of popularity in the 1880s, even though it had been roundly attacked by the physician, poet, and novelist Oliver Wendell Holmes in his 1842 book *Homeopathy and Kindred Delusions*. By this century, however, it seemed to be dying out in the U.S. Its revival began in the late 1980s, under the umbrella of the New Age.

In Europe, homeopathy thrived from its inception, particularly in France, Germany, and Britain. It was given extra respectability in 1849 by the foundation of the Royal London Homoeopathic Hospital, which today has Queen Elizabeth II as its patron. Several European countries make homeopathy available on their national health services, and European Community legislation has been proposed which would exempt homeopathic remedies from double-blind testing.

A similar movement is under way in the U.S. The American Civil Liberties Union decided in 1991 to take a patient class action suit to the Supreme Court over the withdrawal of a North Carolina doctor's license by the state's medical licensing board, because he practiced homeopathy.

Horticulture

Traditionally, horticulture refers to the growing of fruits and vegetables as food, and flowers, flowering shrubs, and trees grown for their beauty.

Commercial horticulture has grown from a hobby or small business to a major industry now very much on a par with many sectors of arable agriculture. Although the land area involved is much smaller than for the traditional agricultural crops such as potatoes, wheat, and corn, horticulture demands a higher technology input and an appreciably higher financial investment in the production of each crop.

Because the value of many of these crops is high and their weight slight, a worldwide air-freight industry has been established to meet year-round demands, making obsolete the phrase "in season." The cut flowers sold in New York City may come from Colombia; the trees and shrubs offered in Oregon may have been grown in Florida. To meet competition from foreign countries, American growers have expanded the use of greenhouses to extend their growing seasons.

High-tech greenhouses

Far from simply providing protection from frost, snow, and other unfavorable weather conditions, greenhouses can be warmed, and more recently have been equipped with powerful lighting, both to allow tropical plants to be grown in a temperate climate and to permit year-round production of temperate zone horticultural crops.

Greenhouses equipped with artificial lighting not only extend growing seasons but increase the yield of crops in all seasons. Under 24-hour lighting, for example, the yield of roses can be doubled. But such lighting is expensive to buy, install, and operate. Research now in progress aims to find the right balance between the costs of lighting and the expected profit, and determine when, in the life cycle of the plant, additional lighting offers the most benefit.

While hobbyists often use fluorescent lighting on indoor plants, commercial growers prefer high intensity discharge lighting – the kind used in street lamps – which is up to 33 per cent more efficient. They are also working with utility companies to try to schedule artificial lighting during "off-peak" hours when rates are lower. Eventually, greenhouse lighting may be controlled by computers that take into account utility rates, the brightness of natural light, and the plants' stage of growth.

Yields of many crops have been greatly increased by boosting the level of carbon dioxide (the atmospheric gas that plants convert into sugars and starch through photosynthesis) inside

Above: The wide range of flowers currently available is largely the result of selective breeding of novel wild plants such as this *Crocus sieberi*, photographed by a horticulturalist at an altitude of 6500ft (2000m) in the mountains of Turkey. The "gene bank" offered by such plants is a valuable resource, since by studying their genetic properties, it is possible to breed new varieties which have, for example, improved frost resistance.

Above: Commercial horticulture demands crops of uniformly high quality, with predictable timing, illustrated here by a stand of cabbages at an experimental research station, almost ready for harvest.

greenhouses. By boosting the CO_2 concentration to provide as much of the gas as the plants can absorb, growers have almost doubled yields of greenhouse-grown tomatoes and cucumbers in the last decade.

Ongoing research programs continue to seek a balance between product quality and concerns about pollution and water conservation. It is important to know how much water a crop needs, and when it should be applied through irrigation. Similarly, the excessive application of nitrate fertilizers has led to water pollution problems. Researchers are seeking to determine plants' nitrogen needs and ensure that sufficient nitrogen

Left and right: The identification and isolation of the gene responsible has allowed plant breeders to develop this strain of branchless "columnar" apple called "Maypole", ideal for even the most restricted garden. It is seen here at blossom and harvest time.

is applied with no wastage, and timed correctly so that it is fully used by the plant.

Benefits of breeding

Since plants were first cultivated, growers have sought to improve yields, size, and quality. Initially this was achieved by selecting only the best specimens from a crop and sowing their seeds. Then came the crossing of top quality plants in an attempt to combine the best features of each.

Until recently, breeding was hit-and-miss, with thousands of progeny being raised to see if the desirable characteristics had been incorporated. Now researchers are "mapping" chromosomes, establishing the location of gene sequences for desirable characteristics. Genetic engineering technology dramatically expands the possibilities; it allows, for example, the transfer of potent genetic resistance to insect attack from one plant family to another completely unrelated one.

Particularly in flowering plants and shrubs, the efforts of plant breeders are visible when comparing the wild originals with the range of glamorous cultivars now available. Today's plant breeders concentrate not only on quality and productivity, but also on building in natural pest and disease resistance so pesticide usage may be minimized.

• FACT FILE •

- Cut flowers and ornamental plants and shrubs, once sold only in specialty stores, now appear in supermarkets and mass merchandising department stores everywhere. To provide the increased volume and low cost these markets demand, growers and distributors have been forced to mechanize.

- Seeding in flats is speeded up by devices that range from simple boxes with rows of holes in them to elaborate machines that use vacuum nozzles to pick up individual seeds, compressed air to deposit them in the soil, and electric eyes to count them. Such machines can place up to 60,000 seeds per hour.

- Some growers seed in "plug flats" made of thin plastic sheets into which hundreds of small cylindrical compartments have been formed. The compartments are filled with soil and seeding machines place one or more seeds in each compartment. When seedlings are large enough for their roots to hold the soil together the plugs are pulled out and transplanted to pots, which have been filled with soil by other machines. Now in development are automated transplanting machines.

- Just as mechanization has brought the end of the family farm, these and other changes may put small growers out of business. "Mom and Pop" operations may not be able to afford to invest in seeding and potting machines, artificial lighting, and other innovations.

Immunology

Immunology, the study of the normal and abnormal functioning of the immune system, is a very young science. In the last 15 years there have been many new and dramatic discoveries. The heart of the subject has been to find out what it is about infections that the body recognizes as foreign; how does it discriminate between "self" and "non-self"?

Foreign invading organisms – parasite, bacterial and viral infections – are very similar to our own tissues. They, like us, are covered with a "coat" which includes proteins. But our immune system has evolved a mechanism which can distinguish between our own proteins and those which belong to someone else. If a foreign invader is spotted, molecules called *antibodies* are hurriedly designed to match its characteristics and put it out of action. Sadly, some people's immune systems treat their own tissue as foreign and respond, causing diseases such as diabetes and arthritis. Others fail, and do not see rogue cells which go on to develop into cancers.

Two types of lymphocytes

Lymphocytes, the cells of the immune system, come in two forms: *B lymphocytes* and *T lymphocytes*. The B lymphocyte (B cell) population can make millions of different antibody molecules capable of recognizing all pathogens (harmful agents). But there is not enough room in the genetic material, the cells' DNA, for the number of genes necessary to make so many molecules.

In fact, genetic diversity is generated by splicing and rearranging the DNA in each B cell. This extraordinary process is called *somatic mutation*, which means that the rearranged DNA is not transferred to future generations. For example, just because our mothers had measles, we are not ourselves immune to it. In 1988, Mark Davis and his group at Stanford University in California discovered that genetic diversity in the T-cell population is generated in the same way.

There are, in turn, two types of T lymphocytes: *cytotoxic T cells* and *helper T cells*. Cytotoxic T cells constantly monitor the proteins on cells, and those that are different, such as virus-infected or cancerous cells, are killed directly. Helper T cells help B cells to make antibodies and encourage the cytotoxic T cells to kill. Without this action, the killing and antibody production would be minimal.

To respond correctly and to our benefit, our immune system must learn to be tolerant of our own proteins (*self proteins*) and cells, yet respond to foreign ones (*non-self*). This education takes place in an organ above the heart called the *thymus*.

In 1987, Philippa Marrack and John Kappler from the Howard Hughes Medical Institute in Denver demonstrated that for a cell to develop into a T cell, it must pass through the thymus. There the T cells interact with all the proteins they are likely to see in the body. Marrack and Kappler showed that if the interaction is too strong the cells die, and if they do not interact the cells still die. Thus, we end up with a population of T cells that respond exclusively and weakly to self proteins.

When these cells circulate in the blood and lymph and through the organs of our bodies, they see again all the self proteins and they know that all is well. Both types of immune cells must recognize non-self to generate an immune response, T cell help being necessary for both antibody production and killing by T cells. This usually ensures that no response is mounted against self. If, however, they see something foreign then they respond with speed and vigor, and eliminate the intruder.

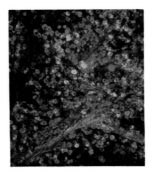

Left: Tissue from a mouse spleen magnified 1000 times. The sample has been treated to reveal two separate types of cell, colored red or green, each of which produces one sort of antibody protein. No cell is both red and green, indicating that the immune reponse is highly specific.

Right: Many of the tests that are done during pregnancy to make sure that the developing baby is healthy depend on specific antibodies. If the mother is rhesus negative and the baby is rhesus positive, the mother is usually treated with anti-rhesus antibodies when the baby is born. This removes any of the baby's red blood cells which would otherwise have "immunized" the mother against rhesus-positive red blood cells making a second pregnancy almost impossible.

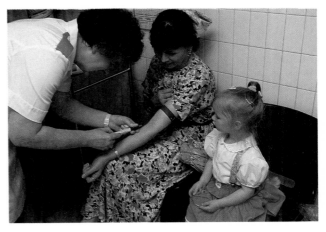

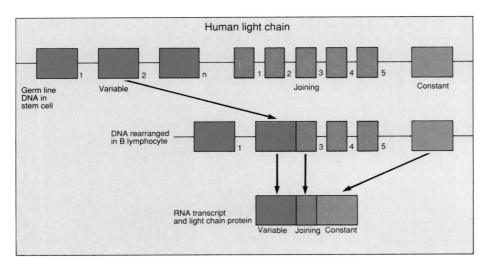

Human light chain

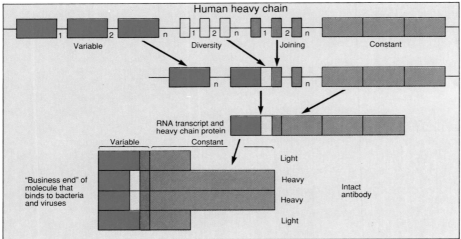

Human heavy chain

Top left: How a huge variety of antibody cells are made. An antibody must vary substantially at its pathogen-binding end but remain unaltered at the other end. It is now known that two genes, the antibody heavy and light chain genes, are needed to make a single antibody molecule. These are discontinuous in their embryonic form, being composed of separated variable (blue) and constant (purple) regions within their DNA. In fact, in the light chain two gene segments are needed for the variable portion of the protein. During early B-cell development a rearrangement of antibody DNA places one of the many alternative variable regions with one of the alternative J segments (pink). This C–J rearranged DNA, along with its constant region, is then used to make RNA.

Above: Heavy chain rearrangement is similar to but more complex than the light chain. An additional family of genetic elements, the diversity segments (gray), must also combine with variable and J segments. Finally, the two chains, heavy and light, combine to form the complete antibody molecule.

Because of the remarkable process of somatic mutation by which antibodies are generated, our immune system has the potential to respond to all pathogens, both known and unknown. We each have, approximately, a billion lymphocytes in our bodies at any one time. There will, however, only be a few (between one and ten) of each B or T cell that are specific to any individual pathogen. Once these cells encounter their bacteria, virus, or parasite, they divide rapidly so that within a few days there will be many thousands of specific cells.

It takes a few days for an antibody response to an influenza virus, for example, to reach levels which can slow down the spread of the virus. As soon as these levels are high enough and there are

enough cytotoxic T cells to kill infected cells, the virus is rapidly cleared from the body. If the same virus tries to invade the same person a second time there will now be many hundreds of immune cells ready to respond immediately.

The immune system adapts and will "remember" that it has seen the particular pathogen before. It will then respond much more vigorously when the same pathogen tries to invade again. This ability of the immune system to adapt and remember is why you will rarely get chicken pox twice and it is how immunization works. By injecting inactive forms of the pathogens that cause polio, diptheria, tetanus, measles, whooping cough, or rubella, each of these populations of cells will be expanded.

The viruses that cause influenza and colds, however, have developed the knack of rapidly changing their appearance, thus causing epidemics of, say, "Russian" flu or "Hong Kong" flu among the human population. Andrew McMichael and his group at the John Radcliffe Hospital in Oxford, U.K., showed in the 1980s that evolution-

Top right: The immune system in action. The same stem cells can turn into lymphocytes, red blood cells, granulocytes, or platelets. Lymphocytes become either B cells or T cells – that is, in the bone marrow or thymus. Two types of T cell come from the thymus – T-helper and T-cytotoxic. T-helper cells help cytotoxic cells to kill bacteria, virus-infected, or tumor cells. They also help B lymphocytes to make antibodies that mediate killing bacteria and viruses. Right: Diabetes occurs when T-helper cells wrongly recognize molecules on the surface of b-islet cells, which make insulin in the pancreas, as foreign. They then help cytotoxic T cells to kill these b-islet cells and help B cells to make antibodies that also mediate killing of the β-islet cells. So as the immune system reponds to b-islet cells. insulin

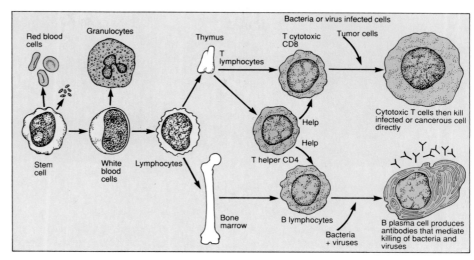

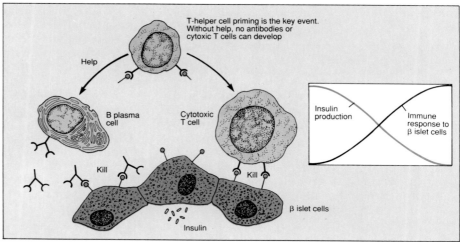

ary pressure on influenza viruses has given them a cunning way of avoiding the adaptive nature of our immune systems. Variants of the virus develop with mutations in the DNA that code for the proteins on their outer coat. This has the effect of tricking the immune system because, although it is the same influenza or cold virus, it looks different from the outside. Our immune system has to go through the same process of expanding the few reactive cells up to a level that can once again repel the unwanted invader.

AIDS — immunodeficiency
People infected with the HIV-1 AIDS virus have shown us how necessary our immune system is to us. This virus infects and kills helper T lymphocytes, thus removing the very cells that would have led to its own destruction.

The AIDS sufferer is, therefore, more prone to common infections such as colds, influenza, pneumonia, and candida, and has no mechanism to prevent cancerous cells from growing. Unfortunately,

immunologists have not yet devised a way of ridding an immune system of the AIDS virus.

Transplantation
If you receive a kidney from another individual your immune system knows that it is not yours, because the cells of the transplanted kidney have proteins on their surface that are like your own but different enough to be recognized as non-self.

Fortunately for the many people who need new organs, there are drugs that will prevent the immune system from rejecting the new material. It is now clear that most of these drugs depend on preventing all lymphocyte function. This can make the individual more susceptible to infections and to cancer.

Autoimmunity
Sometimes, the immune system responds to itself as if it were foreign. For reasons that are also not clear, the immune system breaks self tolerance and overcomes the education it had in the thymus.

Left: Electron micrograph of *Haemophilus influenzae* bacteria (light blue in this false-color image), which can cause pneumonia and bronchitis, on human nose tissue. Image is magnified 250,000 times.

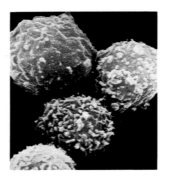

Left: B lymphocytes, magnified 2000 times. These play a crucial role in the human immune system as their surface membranes bear antibodies, called immunoglobulins, which act as receptors to specific antigens on foreign substances.

Diabetes is caused by the immune system recognizing as foreign some of the proteins expressed on the cells that make insulin (*β-islet cells*). Helper T cells help B cells make auto-reactive antibodies against these insulin-producing cells. These, in combination with other proteins in the blood, known as complement, proceed to kill the β-islet cells.

• FACT FILE •

- It is now known that there are more than 100 different types of *rhinovirus* – the major causative agent of the common cold. Like AIDS and flu, rhinoviruses can change their outer coat by mutations of their proteins. What looks to the immune system to be a new virus is actually the same old cold virus inside looking different from the outside.

- In 1986 a team of researchers at Wisconsin led by Barbara Sherry showed that these mutations are greatest in the parts of the molecules that are recognized by the immune system. The mutations in the coat proteins drift in the population and small changes accumulate. Then there is a sudden shift and an entirely new virus coat appears. That is why we all suffer from colds over and over again.

- The search for a vaccine has focused on the parts of the outer coat of the virus that cannot change because they have a specific function. A particular protein in the coat binds very tightly to another protein that is found on almost all the cells of our body. Researchers hope that by learning more about this molecule they may eventually be able to formulate a vaccine for one of humankind's greatest irritants.

Cytotoxic T cells are helped to respond to β-islet cells as if they were cancerous or infected with a virus. These T cells will then kill the insulin-producing cells directly. The end result is the same as if the immune system had been responding to a virus infection.

Arthritis is caused by a similar process with the immune system responding to molecules that form the structures of our joints. The T and B lymphocyte responses generate molecular messages that recruit cells which cause inflammation, swelling, pain, heat, and redness.

Psoriasis, asthma, and multiple sclerosis are all examples of the immune system causing disease by recognizing self components as foreign. Most of the drugs available treat the symptoms rather than the cause of these diseases: insulin for diabetes or anti-inflammatory drugs for arthritis. General immunosuppressive drugs suppress all immune responses and make one more vulnerable to infections.

Monoclonal antibodies

Antibodies are highly specific. They can distinguish between similar but non-identical molecules with ease. This makes them invaluable in many other scientific disciplines: BIOCHEMISTRY, MOLECULAR BIOLOGY, PHYSIOLOGY, PHARMACOLOGY, CELL BIOLOGY, and in medical diagnosis and therapy.

B cells can be taken from the body and grown but they only live for a short while. They can, however, be fused with long lived cancer cells which grow well. These hybrid cells continue to produce antibodies which can be isolated and produced in large quantities. Each B cell makes antibodies specific for only one molecule. The antibodies produced in this way are known as monoclonal antibodies. Nicknamed "magic bullets", these have many uses in medicine and diagnosis.

They can, for example, establish the correct blood type for transfusions. It is possible to make monoclonal antibodies which will target and kill specific tumor cells which have unique molecules on their surface. A monoclonal antibody can prevent endotoxic shock, which is caused by a bacterial infection in the blood.